THE SENSE OF SELF METHOD WORKBOOK

ANTOINETTA VOGELS

HealthySenseOfSelf Publications

HealthySenseOfSelf
www.healthysenseofself.com

Email: contact@healthysenseofself.com

Disclaimer/Notice

The information herein is for the purpose of providing inspiration for personal development through gaining self-knowledge and should not be used as psychological, psychiatric, or mental health advice or counselling.

Production & Editing by Deborah Drake and Nora Tamada

Cover by Marco Scozzi • **Illustrations** by Laura Vogels

To find out more about Healthy Sense of Self® **visit:** https://healthysenseofself.com

Do you have what it takes to be your Self?

The Sense of Self Method,
a self-help, self-healing program for YOU,
because you want nothing more and nothing less than
to become and stay
your Self!

The workbook is based on my book
Healthy Sense of Self: The Secret to Being Your Best Self

Dedication

This revised course material is dedicated especially to those of us
whose essence was neglected or denied as a child.
And to those of us who doubt we are allowed
to count ourselves among the "others" who seem to be okay with who they are.
And to those who have constructed
a maze of coping mechanisms to deal with what others seem to do so effortlessly:
living life.
May the truths you are about to discover serve
as fairytale breadcrumbs that turn into shiny crystals
reflecting the sun and moon's generous light and mark your path
back to your Self.

Table of Contents

A Note from the Author

**DISCOVER THE ZILLION GOOD REASONS TO WORK THE
SENSE OF SELF METHOD WORKBOOK!**

To have or not to have a **Healthy Sense of Self**? That is the question. It is *your* question and it requires an answer—and possibly even action—from *you*.

Do you wonder what a **Sense of Self** actually is?

If it is something missing in you that you never had in the first place, it is only logical that you don't know much about it. If you always had it but were not aware of it, you wouldn't know about it either. A Healthy Sense of Self comes down to knowing you are your own person, that the life you are living is yours and yours alone, and that you have the right to lead your life on your terms.

The Sense of Self Method helps you become aware of why this doesn't always happen and what you can do about it. It is based on our online course of the same name. It is meant as just another gateway to the Sense of Self Method and works perfectly well standing independently.

In both, you will find a description of the SoS Method and how to apply this method to yourself. That way, you hand yourself the tools to finally learn how to live your life on your own terms.

Before I started to investigate my own **Motivations**, I was like a rudderless boat caught in the ebb and flow of events and totally at the mercy of what happened around me and *within* me. I was stuck in reaction mode. When things didn't go my way I would blow up and blame the world and everyone in it.

Writing my book saved me from all that negativity. Reading my (own) book still brings me back to who I am deep down inside. It reminds me that I am a living person, just like everybody else, that there is nothing wrong with me, and that I really don't need to have things just so! Therefore, there is no reason for me to get all worked up when life takes a different turn—**go with the flow** is my new motto.

Are you happy with the choices you make on a daily basis? If not, the Sense of Self (SoS) Method is for you. All you have to do is follow the path I am laying out for you here and you will find yourself able to make different choices that lead to different outcomes; your quality of life will improve drastically as well as your overall success rate!

Here is what you have to do:

1. Set aside 30 minutes every day.

2. Be determined to give it *your all* as you make your way through the workbook so you can start enjoying the many benefits of healing your inner self. Get rid of unwanted conditioning that keeps leading you to the same unwanted results. Become your very own person and get the results *you* want!

Are you ready to stop standing in your own way? Are you ready to step out of the prison of living up to other people's needs and expectations? Are you ready to finally be in charge of your life and your Self?

This course is both a first step toward getting there and a lasting resource to prevent you from slipping back into old habits. It is tough to take charge of your Self but the outcome is worth the hard work. I was able to do it, and so can you. Think of who you would be and what you would be able to realize when you truly are the *master* of your own life.

What if you could exploit all this potential you feel you have within your Self? How would it feel if you were able to sing your song? Imagine the satisfaction of using your potential to the fullest, cultivating your relationships to the max, and raising your children in such a way that you stay friends for life. All of that and much more results from working the Sense of Self Workbook now!

Online you can find the Sense of Self Method Course on our website

at https://healthysenseofself.com. The online course is enlivened and completed by multiple videos that provide additional explanation. By giving this hard copy version, we hope to reach more people and facilitate the needs of those who work better with a physical book.

If you have any questions, please do not be shy. Shoot us an email at: courses@ healthysenseofself.com. Let us know what you need, how we can help you grow, and ultimately become the best version of your Self. We want you to have the experience that best fits your needs in your search for the solution to whatever it is that made you decide to buy this book and work through it!

However, please be aware that that last statement is crucial: just buying the book won't bring about the results you wish for—it takes time, effort, and dedication. You have to do the work!

YOU ONLY HAVE ONE LIFE — MAKE SURE IT'S YOURS!

An Overview of this Workbook

Introduction – Do you have what it takes to be your Self?

*In the Introduction, get acquainted with the course and create a
Learning Agreement with your Self.*

The introduction looks into the importance of being able to sense your Self and
has you consider the question of whether you see value in freeing yourself of specific
old behaviors that no longer seem to serve you in the present. Sensing your Self is an
important skill if you want to live your life as the healthy, happy person you know you
can be.

Unit 1 – WHY do you think you do WHAT you do?

*In Unit 1, dig deeper into **WHY** you do **WHAT** you do.*

Unit 1 focuses on getting to the root of your behavior, and explains why that is
important: you can solve many, if not all, of your life issues when you know WHY you
do WHAT you do. Why do you make certain choices and decisions? Becoming aware
of this is especially useful for people who feel they are not completely in charge of their
actions and behavior.

Unit 2 – Whose life is it, anyway?

*In Unit 2, determine the people, both past and present, who have influenced your
life.*

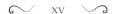

Unit 2 offers insight into the difference between those people who have a Healthy Sense of Self compared to those who are eternally struggling to find themselves. Being born doesn't come with a guarantee that you get to live your own life. This unit helps you answer the question: Do you have a Healthy Sense of Self or a **Lack of Sense of Self**?

Unit 3 – Your past shapes your present. Is your present good enough to shape your future?

In Unit 3, uncover your **Early Childhood Survival Strategies**.

Unit 3 helps you understand what went on in your childhood. The way you were related to by your parents in early childhood affects how you relate to yourself on a subconscious level, and is (in part) responsible for what you make of yourself during your lifetime. If left with an undeveloped Sense of Self, you are set up for failure. Breaking free starts with seeing what really happened.

Unit 4 – "Thinks" are seldom what they seem

In Unit 4, investigate your Motivations.

Unit 4 introduces two categories of motivation identified by the Sense of Self Method: **Direct Motivation** and **Indirect Motivation**.

Understanding your Motivation requires awareness of what is going on in your subconscious mind. Discerning which kind of Motivation is operating in the background of your various behaviors is the key to self-knowledge, to healing a Lack of Sense of Self, and to gaining a **Restored Sense of Self**.

Unit 5 – Are you using your life to prove that you are okay?

In Unit 5, discover what **Vehicles** are supporting your **Ego-References**.

Unit 5 addresses why certain things play such a dominant role in your life and what is behind that. When you are unable to develop a (Healthy) Sense of your Self, you adopt ways of behaving to gain acceptance from the people you *believe* you need approval from. Two new key concepts—Ego-References and Vehicles—will help you discover how your past is influencing your present.

UNIT 6 – THE NEED TO "FEEL-GOOD-ABOUT-SELF" CAN BE COMPULSIVE

In Unit 6, learn to recognize your **Hidden Agenda** *and* **Hidden Goal***, and what makes you* **"Feel-good-about-self."**

Unit 6 investigates what drives you to crave approval and introduces a few processes that contribute to the subconscious drama at play in those with a Lack of Sense of Self. You will discover how to shift from being focused on gaining approval to focusing on what YOU want your life to be like, based on your own conscious decisions.

UNIT 7 – "WILL I EVER OUTGROW THE NEED FOR APPROVAL?"

In Unit 7, begin to understand your **Internalized Parental Voice** *and the messages it sends you.*

Unit 7 delves deeper into the role parental judgment can play in your life. Caregivers need not even be present for their opinions to linger in your mind and body. You will learn about the entanglement of parent/caregiver and child that is both the cause and the result of a Lack of Sense of Self, which puts you at risk for a lifetime of emotional exhaustion and suffering.

UNIT 8 – "HELP ME, MOTHER! I SENSE MY SELF DISAPPEARING WHEN I DON'T SUCCEED IN MAKING YOU HAPPY!"

In Unit 8, explore the concept of **Annihilation***.*

Unit 8 brings all the information of the previous units together and clarifies what the Sense of Self Theory—and Method—are all about. Building on what you have learned so far, you will now see a structure you may have unconsciously created that functions as the placeholder for the Real Self-experience. This unit poses the question: Whose happiness really matters most to you?

UNIT 9 – PORTRAIT OF A SUBSTITUTE SoS–ORIENTED LIFE

In Unit 9, map out your **Substitute Sense of Self–Oriented System**.

Unit 9 leads you through each of the course concepts as they could apply to you. Once you manage to understand the origins of each of these elements, you will be able to effectively create lasting changes and finally break free from your addiction to approval.

Introduction
Do you have what it takes to be your Self?

WELCOME TO THE SENSE OF SELF METHOD

Would you say you are a person who places a lot of value on the approval of others in order to feel good about yourself? And, if you are answering yes, do you ever wonder where that need for approval came from? If your answer is yes again, then this workbook offers you an opportunity to discover the roots of this need and then something even bigger and more important.

The purpose of this workbook is to help you help yourself to fully become your own person. When you leave behind all traces of the need to get other people's approval, you can fully be yourself and live your life based on your own potential.

Each unit will feature a specific lesson to help you develop an understanding of the Theory behind the Sense of Self Method and get clear insight into the nature of your own Sense of Self. This course will lead you step by step to truly understand yourself and open the door (for you) to make different choices in crucial life-directing matters, which can lead to considerable improvement in your quality of life.

We invite you to consider this overarching question as you begin this workbook: Do you think it is useful or necessary for you to free yourself of specific old behaviors that no longer serve you in the present?

BENEFITS OF GAINING A HEALTHY SENSE OF SELF

At the beginning of each Unit, clear-cut benefits will be pointed out so you know what you can look forward to when you have completed the course.

Three benefits you could gain from having a Healthy—or Restored— Sense of Self are:

- Being happier in all aspects of your life
- Better chance to find, give, and receive love
- Better overall health

GLOSSARY

Each unit of this workbook focuses on several key terms that are best understood in a progressive and interconnected order. For your convenience, a Glossary of terms used in this workbook is included in the Appendices.

The glossary on the website includes some additional terms not addressed in this course, and contains links to extended and more detailed information on each term.
https://healthysenseofself.com/glossary/

NEW SENSE OF SELF TERMS

In each unit you will learn two or three of the 40+ terms that are specific to the SoS Method. Familiarize yourself with these concepts as they will help you identify and modify what, so far, has been covered up by your missing understanding of the mystery of your own inner workings.

The SoS Method's Key Terms will use the following abbreviations.

SoS – Sense of Self
HySoS – Healthy Sense of Self
SSoS or Substitute SoS – Substitute Sense of Self
LoSoS – Lack of Sense of Self
Fgas – "Feel-good-about-self"
EgoRef – Ego-Reference
ECSS – Early Childhood Survival Strategy
QoL level – Quality-of-Life level
RestSoS – Restored Sense of Self
IPV – Internalized Parental Voice

Our first Sense of Self (SoS) term is:

Healthy Sense of Self

The ability to experience and be present to your own person and to your own life and recognize both as uniquely owned by YOU. That includes the right to live and be as your Self and experience your innermost core as your ultimate home from where you live your life.

You have enough self-awareness, personal power, and presence of mind to make choices based on your own preferences, tastes, and values, regardless of the influences of parents, teachers, peers, and society.

The skill of Being Your Self is often taken for granted. Some people can do it, while others have no idea how to be themselves. And a third group is convinced they are being their genuine, authentic self, but only because they don't know the difference.

This course is ideal if you have doubts about knowing who you really are. Maybe you feel something is off in your deepest sense about yourself, but you can't say exactly what it is. Taking this course will make you better equipped to create and maintain a positive relationship with your Self.

If you do not have a problem being yourself, it'll help you understand what others go through at times—maybe your friend or loved one, or even a customer or client—this course could give you the edge you've been looking for and result in you dealing with others in more positive and constructive ways.

Please stay open to exploring the nature of your Sense of Self, even if you feel doubt or reluctance—and especially if you feel resistance!

Consider the possibility that your Sense of Self is not as healthy as you think it is, and if you discover that is the case for you, know that the situation can be remedied.

GUIDING QUESTIONS

Each unit will have a selection of questions and prompts to guide you into looking deeper within your Self and your history. These will help you get acquainted with your Self and discover the roots of your Motivations and Hidden Goals.

READING SELECTIONS

In each unit we offer selected readings from the SoS book *Healthy Sense of Self: The Secret to Being Your Best Self.*

READING SELECTIONS FROM *HEALTHY SENSE OF SELF* – INTRODUCTION

Excerpts from the Preface

THE START OF MY INNER QUEST

The development of the Sense of Self Method began nearly 30 years ago merely as my personal quest, as a new mother, to end insomnia. Now, this book represents part of a growing business, research, and educational project. Publishing this Method is the realization of my vision to contribute to a better life for each individual on a personal level, and on a bigger scale for the world at large.

It is 1985, and my daughter is three months old; it is time to return to work. I have a job as a bassoonist in the Amsterdam Philharmonic Orchestra, and the six weeks of maternity leave have come to an end. Why am I suddenly unable to drift off into a well-deserved and refreshing sleep, just when I need it most? Being a new mother is quite a challenge by itself, especially when your child is born prematurely. She was as tiny as a Barbie doll, my first-born. Combining the care of my baby with being in shape for my job required a clear mind and a well-rested body, but no… I can't sleep!

"No doubt I'm having trouble adjusting to my new situation. I trust it will gradually solve itself," I reassured myself. But it didn't. One night I would sleep reasonably well and the next two nights there would be little or no sleep at all. Not that I actually worried about something while lying in bed; no, my mind was totally blank. Nothing stirred. I had no idea what was going on.

In the months that followed the onset of this insomnia, I tried to cope in many ways. "Have a glass of hot milk before you go to bed," was my mother's advice. "A glass of red wine," a well-meaning friend suggested. "Stop doing anything an hour before you go to bed and do relaxation exercises," was someone else's advice. "No coffee for you!" I was ordered by many people. "No garlic and no peppers," was the remedy from a Tibetan healer, along with his prescription of a great number of bitter *brown pills that made no difference. My doctor provided me with sleep medications, and yes, they did put me to sleep. But the moment I stopped taking them, it was over. I did not sleep anymore. As medical causes for my constant insomnia were ruled out, I despaired: "What else is left for me now but a lifetime of medication?"*

I refused to start on that journey. I figured that sleeping is a natural process and if my sleep was being thwarted, there had to be a reason. I was determined to discover that reason. So I turned inward in my quest for the cause and the cure of what kept me awake at night and that was so damaging to my quality of life. It affected my ability to mother my child, maintain my health and resume my career, not to mention what it was doing to our family life.

In hindsight, I can say that I had more problems than just insomnia. They included an extreme temper. If things did not go the way I wanted, I would burst out in anger and blame everyone and the world for it. Even my best friend expressed her concern about my temper. My co-musicians complained that they felt I lacked team spirit. I had frequent colds on crucial performance days and a sore throat whenever I made a commitment to sing. "Your timing is off in ensemble-playing," my colleagues pointed out candidly.

I tried changing things outside myself: practicing like crazy, taking more lessons, getting help at home. Not a thing I tried had the desired result; as looking outside of me didn't really help with the problems, gradually I began to observe what was going on inside of me. I started to observe my thoughts and behavior. I delved deeper into all the things I was worrying about instead of pushing them away. "What are my motives for what I do or for what I try to avoid?" I wondered. What was the underlying reason was for my explosions of rage, which seemed so out of proportion to what actually took place on those moments.

A Mini-Disc recorder became my confidante. I began to record my thoughts and feelings, and sometimes I listened to what I had said. For 25 years, I talked to and studied myself, trying to make sense of what motivated me and I noticed that often I seemed to work against, instead of in favor of, my personal goals and ambitions. I discovered my choices were based on subconscious, not conscious, motives. Decades later, an understanding emerged about what was really going on in my mind that previously had been totally outside the spotlight of my awareness. I was shocked time and again to find what I started to call my Hidden Agenda.

I discovered that I had motives that I had never considered. Some of the emotions I experienced on a daily basis were reactions to things I had no conscious awareness of. To my surprise, I realized I had many fears. So I followed the trail back to the roots of my fears and I learned what kept me imprisoned and why certain motives were still as active in me as when I was a child or an adolescent. I had yet to understand the reasons for my fears or for my insomnia. All I was able to create was a map, and as we all know, "The map is not the territory." However, this map has proved very useful to me in changing the territory of my life, both internally and externally.

*Many years later, I was able to describe the nature of many of my problems; I had to conclude that they stemmed from an unhealthy relationship with my mother. Unknowingly, an **Enmeshment** had formed between the woman who had raised me and me. This state of Enmeshment prevented me from developing any sense of being an independent and autonomous person. It kept me spellbound to try to live up to her conditions.*

SOMETHING WAS MISSING: MY SENSE OF SELF

In my search for the truth that would enable me to break free from my predicament, the discovery I made was quite unexpected, and one that I dreaded to even say aloud. It was the hardest truth I ever had to face, and even now when I think about how the ways of the world seem to trample people's holiest places, it chills my heart. The role and function of a mother is revered, and therefore I had great difficulty finding support among my family (father, brother, and sister) and even among friends, in contemplating the possibility that there might be any fault in the relationship between my mother and me. Even the Bible protects her: "Honor your father and your mother," one of the commandments states. But how can we respectfully find a solution if things do not follow the commonly accepted picture of all-encompassing love?

Can we even allow ourselves to look at the (our) mother and find that she is just a person who has her own demons to fight? Should we not admit that, unless the mother is able and willing to get a clear sense of her shortcomings, she will not be able to attend to the needs of her child in a sufficient or optimal way. What I found was that I had never felt acknowledged and respected as a (valued) unique human being but that I had been treated as a pawn in her own game of life, which had thwarted in me the development of a Healthy Sense of Self.

Instead of having an inner "home base" for my "me-ness," I depended on getting approval, mainly from my mother but also my father. Sometimes it wasn't my mother but a replacement for them, like another "authority figure," who triggered in me the same need to feel accepted. Sometimes it just was, what I call, "virtual parental approval," as I had internalized most of their opinions and judgments, having been focused on them throughout my life.

My life was quite an emotional jungle. My journey was mainly about finding my way through this entanglement by constantly scrutinizing and interpreting my symptoms—at whatever moments I could get out of the whirlpool of being absorbed by them. This task took over my life and by and by led me to follow a different path. This book is the result of that process.

Since then, my quality of life has gone way up. I am happier, healthier, more playful, and more successful. Occasionally I fall back, as I still need to refresh my reconditioning every so often. Through that, I can reach again, on the deepest level, the certainty that my being and my doing are separate. In order to be I do not have to do; in order to do I first have to be; then I have the choice of doing or not doing. My Being is no longer correlated with, or dependent on my Doing.

I can say wholeheartedly that every day, getting into the right mind-set and experiencing my Restored Sense of Self comes more easily. It needs to be said: My method of restoring one's Sense of Self is not a quick fix. However, everything is better than skipping your own life altogether— and honestly, it is mighty interesting as well!

I feel moved to share my story and my findings in the hope and expectation that you will find value in it. This sharing has required devoting myself nearly full-time for several years to developing the materials you are seeing. What motivated me to put in so much effort?

I have learned in the course of my healing process that we can break the vicious cycle, which perpetuates an unhealthy SoS from one generation to the next, by making our own SoS healthier. Once we will have taken care of our own SoS, we will be able to effectively facilitate a healthy SoS in our children. Then everyone's quality of life will improve considerably. There will be less violence, less war, less human suffering. I take pride in reporting about my life's journey so others can learn from my experiences and thus make this world a better place.

Sharing my findings with you, with the world, also fulfills a vow I made as a four-year-old girl looking at the ruins of World War II.

MY VOW AS A LITTLE GIRL

I was born in the Netherlands right after World War II. Even though I was not alive during the war, I vividly recall listening to my father's stories about the horrors that happened during the Holocaust. I remember walking with him over the ruins of the city in which he was born and raised, Groningen (see Figure P.1). I have stored in my memory in detail the atrocious acts of war I picked up on with my four-year-old ears. Is it a wonder that my firm decision, my vow to myself that I had to do something to make wars stop, was firmly engraved in my mind, even though I was just a little girl?

Little did I know that life would offer me an opportunity to contribute to the understanding of human behavior by having me grow up with a Lack of Sense of Self. Through the task of figuring out what was "off" in my life, I gained a deep understanding of what is "off" with the world and, with that, of what could be the healing procedure.

Now, more than half a century later, my vow is ready to start its work. My contribution to humanity is to help bring peace in the family, peace among people in general. My Sense of Self Method greatly helps to establish peace within the heart and mind of each individual. When we have a clear SoS, we can find peace within ourselves. Only when we have peace within ourselves we are able to solve conflicts with others in a non- violent way.

My findings are the fruits of my life experience and intense effort to understand the ultimate cause of my personal problems. The root cause of these problems (and possibly yours) is quite similar to the root cause of war. By studying the SoS Method, you will—I believe with all my heart— not only experience a decrease in the number and level of intensity of your own problems, and finally get a good night's sleep, but also contribute to a more peaceful world.

Ending the war within ourselves through gaining a Restored Sense of Self will lead us to happier and more productive lives. Finding our "inner home" may also help prevent wars between people, between nations. I truly hope that the impact of the concepts of this Method is clear and that it may help you and your loved ones to become more successful and live up to your potential.

The essence of this message is that once we gain the ability and the courage to honor our own spirit, we automatically gain an ease about letting others honor theirs, and no fighting is needed to establish who has the power. We can just be who we were born to be.

I truly thank you for having come to this point of reading of how this book was born. Now let us get ready to work our way toward our goal of less human suffering!

The purpose of this work is:

1. *to help people recognize whether they have a **Substitute Sense of Self**;*
2. *to find the cause of why and how this could happen;*
3. *to have people accept and face their condition based on these insights;*
4. *to eliminate the power of their unhealthy past in their present, and*
5. *to ultimately replace their Substitute Sense of Self by a Restored Sense of Self.*

The SoS Method will remain a living work in progress for some time to come. I invite you to share your thoughts, thus helping to turn this educational work from a Method into a practical healing method and giving more people a chance to improve their quality of life.

I salute our journey together. I invite your participation. Please share whatever you think can help implement a healthy SoS for all. To those who want to use the Method for healing purposes: Healing through a self- help method is hard work; I hope that this Method will help you heal faster and with less pain along the way.

This book presents:

- *the SoS Method with extensive explanation, examples, and details;*
- *several methods for self-assessment;*
- *suggestions, exercises, and education for recovery: gaining a Restored Sense of Self (RestSoS).*

WHO MIGHT BENEFIT FROM WORKING WITH THIS METHOD?

It is likely that you will be able to improve the quality of your life if any of the following describe you:

- *Something is "off" but you are unable to find what it is.*
- *You know you are not living up to your potential.*
- *Doctors and therapists don't make you better.*
- *You have relationship challenges: marriage, children, social.*
- *You are addicted to work or other activities or behavior.*
- *You have a terrible time staying sober.*
- *You are in pain physically or emotionally.*

My insight is new, original, and highly unconventional. Who would think that there are people walking around in this life without a SoS? What does that actually imply? Please don't toss out the idea too quickly just because you think it is unusual and therefore probably doesn't apply to you. Or just because you don't like the idea of applying it to yourself—the degree to which denial plays a role in all this is impressive. There are many people, including the majority of Americans, walking around without a healthy and Natural SoS.

We now know that the solution is to restore or strengthen your SoS. Then we are no longer ruled by unhealthy and (in hindsight completely obsolete and unnecessary) subconscious motivations, which too often can be the cause of many problems and pains.

Educating ourselves about, and then healing, our SoS might alleviate an impressive array of problems. An astounding variety of ill health, lack of well-being, general or specific dysfunctions, and in general feeling miserable seem to all come down to the root cause of lacking a healthy SoS. Some of these problems and pains include but are not limited to the following:

- *Headaches Fatigue Anxiety Insomnia Depression*
- *Marital problems*
- *Relationship problems in general*
- *Addictions of many kinds*
- *Relapse during recovery from addiction to substance use*
- *Anger issues and rage*
- *Work-related problems*
- *Being held back by "invisible glass ceilings" Too much drama*
- *Not living up to one's potential*
- *Being high-strung*
- *Lack of focus or learning problems in children*

The symptoms and problems show up differently for each of us and vary with our circumstances. The strength of the SoS Method is that it functions as an umbrella for a great number of ailments and dysfunctions. In other words, the root cause of a lot of dysfunction and disease may, I believe, be greatly relieved by having a Restored Sense of Self (RestSoS).

No pills, potions, doctor's visits, new religion, or new technology is needed, though some people might require assistance or professional help. You are your own expert.

That fact, together with understanding and applying the SoS Method, can give you great tools to solve a variety of issues you might have and deeply enhance your life!

WHAT IS REQUIRED FROM YOU?

Getting to the answer to your challenges requires your open-minded willingness to look around inside your mind and feelings and be honest about what you find. I offer you suggestions of what to look for. If you find what I think you will find, you can apply to yourself the suggestions and solutions that worked for me. The Method is logical and easy to understand. There are stories and examples, and the basics are repeated on a regular basis. Once you get the ideas, you are well on your way to your own healing!

*There also is a chance that you already have a healthy **Natural Sense of Self**. In that case you might want to read the book out of interest or to help understand your clients or even your friends. There is much to learn that can help you do better business with people once you have a clearer view on where they might be coming from.*

THERE IS NO PERFECT SOLUTION BUT...

For many of the problems and choices we face in life, there simply isn't the option to find a one and only best solution. Sometimes we need to set priorities or give in to the limitations of our personal circumstances. But one thing every caregiver can do is this: Consider your children as independent, autonomous human beings and not as extensions of yourself! Having a healthy SoS yourself enables you to do just that. If you feel that is a challenge for you, then please find the courage to undertake the steps necessary to work your own way to a healthy Restored Sense of Self. This will enable you to create a better future for yourself, for your child, and for the world!

In a nutshell, that is the purpose and goal, the hope and the vision, of the SoS Method and the activities of our company, Healthy Sense of Self®.

PROCEED TO THE ACTIVITY THAT FOLLOWS

ACTIVITY

Each unit has an activity that is related to the new key terms and/or to the objective of the unit. These activities work as building blocks for future units.

Your ACTIVITY for the Introduction is to

Create a Learning Agreement between YOU and Your Self!

Become totally aware of your main goal when you decide to use this workbook. Please sit down and write an agreement with your Self to meet this goal. It will set the tone for your experience of this coursework.

CREATE A LEARNING AGREEMENT

Your journey to better understanding yourself has begun with your intention to take this course. We now invite you to create a Learning Agreement with your Self as your first activity. In this section, we offer several formats for creating your Learning Agreement. You may choose to complete all of them for maximum benefit.

Why create a Learning Agreement?

- To understand and remember what motivated you to register.
- To identify and acknowledge your goals and intentions.
- To support you as you navigate material that might challenge you.

Making an agreement with your Self is like a promise. It means you are serious about this course and want to succeed. This promise is more likely to be kept, because:

- You then have a reminder of this promise to your Self.
- What you choose for yourself is easier to stay committed to.
- What you declare for yourself is potent.
- What you choose for yourself is what matters most!

Setting goals and intentions will keep you clear, focused, and motivated. How would you complete the following statements?

- I agree to stay open, curious, and committed to choosing and using the exercises and tools offered to improve areas of my life, which are…
- What I want most for myself or someone I care about is…
- The changes I would like to make are… because I feel these behaviors are coping mechanisms and they are not really ME.

FREE-WRITE EXERCISE

Free writing is offered throughout the course—here we introduce some ways to use this powerful tool:

An alternate way to craft an agreement with yourself is to **free-write** your responses to the prompts offered below. If you don't censor yourself, your mind naturally fills in blanks with authentic answers. What you say first is often the truest response you'll give. So make sure you capture that!

1. Some examples of statements to get you started:

- I am taking on discovering my **Real Self**.
- I will do what it takes to be my authentic Self.
- Even though I feel fear, I will answer the question anyway! I am committed to being honest with myself.
- I am determined to find out what is behind my resistance to seeing and accepting certain insights and changing certain perspectives.
- I acknowledge the power of denial and I am willing to investigate more deeply.
- Keep your statements as active and specific and vivid as possible.

2. Alternately, complete the following statements to develop a clear sense of your goals and overarching intentions to assure you will stay committed.

I can be counted on to

_____

_____

_____

_____

_____

_____

I am known for being

_____

_____

_____

_____

I wish I were more

_____

_____

_____

I have always wondered why I

_____

_____

_____

_____

Success to me looks like

_____

_____

_____

I'm done with being the one who always says yes to

_____

_____

_____

_____

It is important to turn off the critic in your head and write quickly, withholding judgment, and acknowledge everything is fair game.

Declare it! Be real! Be truthful! Be bold! Dare to dream big for yourself!

SAMPLE LEARNING AGREEMENT WITH SELF

To inspire you, let me offer you an example of a written Learning Agreement.

"I, Antoinetta, am taking this course so that I FINALLY get clear on why I feel so stressed out and hurried, even when performing minor tasks and attending to minor appointments. I have done so much personal work and there are still those pesky weeds in my garden that return every season. I know I am capable, so why do I sabotage myself?

I know I am appreciated for my generosity, but sometimes I still say yes, when I want to say no.

I will take a stand for my own life.

I will be myself when I am alone or with anyone else.

I am committed to uncovering what is at the root of my need for the acknowledgment of others so I can celebrate my own "awesomeness."

I will plan for procrastination, because I know myself well enough to see that I will delay if I am tired or haven't had enough quiet time with myself.

I look forward to discovering what shifts in thinking and behavior I can make that will make my quality of life so much better and reduce the stress in my life even more."

Now create your own Learning Agreement in your own words.

_____

_____

_____

_____

_____

_____

_____

_____

_____

_____

_____

_____

I commit to restoring my Sense of Self.

Signature: _____

Date: _____

Each unit will contain a quote from our Guided Journal for you to contemplate.

QUOTE FROM THE *GUIDED JOURNAL*

DAY
116

WE, people
with a Healthy Sense of Self
have no need to fight others for fear that they will
take away
our opportunity
to "Feel-good-about-ourselves."

We don't have to get that feeling from outside!
Feeling good about ourselves
is our default state:
We feel alive!

We would like to encourage you to take a few minutes each and every day, to sit down with your Self in mind and experience yourself in your body. Explore how you are feeling. There is no right or wrong. The point is to cultivate your skill of sensing your Self, which will help you to become more convinced that:

You already ARE—you do not have to earn your Self!

RECAP

In each future unit, we will give a recap of the concepts and ideas you were introduced to, followed by a short quiz with a few questions to check whether you have a good understanding of the unit.

RECAP FOR THE INTRODUCTION

We began by having you look into the importance of being able to sense your Self. We had you consider the question of whether you see value in freeing yourself of specific old behaviors that no longer seem to serve you in the present. We encouraged you to take some time to answer questions and create your Learning Agreement with yourself.

Sensing your Self is an important skill to have if you want to live your life as the healthy, happy person you know you can be. Taking this course will lead you to look deeply inside yourself so you can recognize and effectively modify patterns of behavior that, so far, have impeded you from reaching your true potential.

QUIZ

At the end of each unit you will find a number of questions. There are two types of questions:

Some questions relate directly to the content of the lesson and are intended to help you become more proficient in the material. Answers to these questions can be found in the answer key provided at the end of this workbook.

The other questions are meant to help you integrate the material by applying it to your own life. These questions are of a personal nature and cannot be verified through the course as the answers will vary from person to person. You must use your own judgment here.

The key is to be completely honest in your answers. You are the only one who will see them anyway. Think of how the different aspects of your life relate to the questions, things like relationships, family, work, and creative endeavors.

Consider your answers as an important point of departure for taking the course.

QUIZ FOR THE INTRODUCTION

Here are two questions to verify (for yourself) whether you have a good understanding of the concepts of the Introduction:

1. What is a Sense of Self?

_____

_____

_____

_____

2. Why is creating a Learning Agreement with your Self so important?

_____

_____

_____

_____

_____

REFLECTIVE QUESTIONS

Here are three reflective questions to deepen your understanding of the Introduction as it relates to your Self:

1. Do you think you have a Sense of Self? How healthy is it on a scale from 1-10, where 10 is the healthiest?

_____

_____

_____

_____

_____

2. What are the most important aspects of the Learning Agreement you have created with your Self?

_____

_____

_____

_____

3. What are the things you want to change by working your way through this Sense of Self Method Workbook?

_____

_____

_____

_____

_____

LOOKING AHEAD

To finish up, we will look ahead at what will be covered the next unit.

LOOKING AHEAD FOR THE INTRODUCTION

For Unit 1, consider these questions: What is the value of doing what I have always done? Is it just because it's what I know? Do I perhaps identify with this action or behavior? In other words, would I still be ME if I did things differently? How would truly living my own life be different from what I am doing right now?

NOTES

Unit 1
WHY do you think you do
WHAT you do?

The purpose of this course is to give you an understanding of where and why you are unable to remove the emotional roadblocks that prevent you from being the best *you* that you could ever be. After clarifying the theory behind the SoS Method, this course gives you the tools to help free your Self from a lot of unnecessary suffering and become a happier person.

Unit 1 focuses on getting to the root of your behavior, and explains why that is important: you can solve many, if not all, of your life issues when you know WHY you do WHAT you do.

Why do you make certain choices and decisions? There are two layers in this process. In this unit, we deal with the obvious top layer, but be prepared, there might be more to it than you expect.

BENEFITS

Some benefits of Restoring your Sense of Self are:

- More compassion, empathy, tolerance
- Less hostility
- Fewer rages and family upsets
- More patience

NEW SoS TERMS
Who am I? / Sense of Self (SoS)

Who Am I?

This is the ultimate question to ask yourself as you begin a journey of Self-exploration, with the objective of finding out your true (and perhaps unknown) motives for doing or avoiding things.

"Who am I?" is a deceptively simple question. Throughout your life, you go through great changes, and things about who you are don't always make sense. But starting now, you will benefit from knowing more about yourself because not knowing the answer to the question "Who am I?" can make you a victim in your life instead of the Master of your own fate.

You might think at first, "Of course I know who I am: I am a mother, a daughter, an aunt to Johnny, a friend to Eva. I am a carpenter or an engineer; I am someone's fiancé or spouse." But are those really the truest answers to "Who am I?" or, to rephrase, "What am I all about?" Being consciously aware of what it is that makes you get up in the morning, other than the habit of doing so, will give you true insight into who you are—one that is based on your deep, internal motivations.

Sense of Self

A conscious or subconscious awareness of existing independently as a unique and potentially autonomous human being and of what intrinsically comes with it in your daily life.

Does the term "Sense of Self" resonate with you, and if so, how? What does it mean to you, now that you have watched the video for this lesson? Please know that the concept is less about the Self, and more about "Sensing" the Self.

Is the light on in the fridge when I close the door? Does a tree falling in the woods still make noise when I am not there to hear it?

A similar question can be asked about the Self: Is your Self still there when you are not sensing it?

In this course, you will begin learning to Sense your Self, which will enable you to be truer to yourself and make your world a better place!

Consider this: You have a body that you can see and touch and feel—it is proof you exist independently from your caregivers and not as an extension of our parents them. So why then is it possible for you, as a full-grown adult, to feel as if you don't fully control your own life? In fact, you don't just feel you can't—there are mechanisms at work in your mind and emotions that do not allow it to happen: so you really can't!

You hear your heart beating and you feel air filling your lungs when you breathe deeply. It's obvious where these processes happen and you can easily sense when something is off. But where does your Sense of Self reside and how did it come into existence? Is it fully functioning?

GUIDING QUESTIONS

Fill in the rest of each sentence we have started for you here and feel free to use these prompts more than once to come up with different endings.

Ever since I was young I have needed/wanted/loved to

_____

_____

_____

_____

My family has always been/done/cared about

_____

_____

_____

_____

_____

When I feel stressed, I immediately

_____

_____

_____

_____

_____

_____

_____

When I really want something, I will

_____

_____

_____

_____

_____

_____

_____

READING SELECTIONS FROM *HEALTHY SENSE OF SELF* – UNIT 1
Excerpts from Chapter 1

WHY DO YOU THINK YOU DO WHAT YOU DO?

Introduction to the Sense of Self Method

What is it like not to have a Natural Sense of Self? The question is hard to pose, let alone to answer. How is it possible to experience the lack of something you do not know exists in the first place? In the Preface, I extensively described how I found out that I was lacking something other people seemed to have. Let me give you an example of a situation that helped me to see a small light that was going to grow and become a beacon in the jungle of darkness.

"Please don't be mad at me," I kept begging my husband every time I yelled at him to vent my annoyance when I was unable to fall asleep. "In reality I am not angry at you, but I am angry at the fact that I don't sleep. I can't keep myself from getting upset and I need to let it out."

He understood, and so we went on like that for many years. However, at some point he said, "I do not quite understand you. Are you not the one in control of this anger? You either choose to or choose not to be angry. Then, if you do, you choose how to express yourself." I simply could not find within myself any power, force, or will that was capable of such choosing or not choosing. Based on this and other similar conclusions I deduced that he must have something inside that I did not have. So I started to pay attention and look more closely into this.

A Brief Summary of the SoS Method

This Method presents a new and integrated approach to the understanding of an important part of the human condition, and offers potential improvements. My point of departure is that body, mind, and emotions are continuously in communication with each other during all developmental and maturational phases, which then results in the way each person is whatever he or she is in the world right now.

Here is what I believe. Each of us is born with certain qualities and characteristics of who we are when our potential is optimally manifested in life. It is crucial that a person live under conditions that enable this process to take place. In other words, if there are few obstacles to your developing a healthy mind and body, then your life circumstances allow you to live up to your potential. What happens though, if there are too many obstacles? What happens to your potential when your development, as it could naturally go, is blocked or distorted by certain life circumstances (which seem to be the rule rather than the exception)?

I always felt I could have been so much more successful in doing what I have done, if I hadn't been forced to look within to find what was off with me, and how to change into a person who has her act together. If only I had been so lucky not to have been distracted by doing the things for the wrong reason, and to have spent all that energy and focus on my profession or even on being social, I would have been good at it and it would have been worth my education. Or perhaps, I would not have chosen to become a professional musician at all and would have found great satisfaction as a psychologist.

I would have had, possibly, a lot of people who wanted to be my friend because I had something to offer instead of being needy and fearing rejection.

The Importance of a SoS

This Method maintains that:

- *the development of a Natural Sense of Self is a core aspect of healthy, normal psychological maturation;*
- *the maturation of SoS is subject to either healthy or unhealthy development based on behavior of the primary caregiver toward the child;*
- *a lack of a Natural Sense of Self in a person leads automatically to dependency on a Substitute SoS for self- experience, which is one of the root causes of many aspects of human suffering.*

To improve the human condition, it is crucial that all people be educated in developing, strengthening, or restoring a Natural SoS in themselves as well as in their children.

PROCEED TO THE ACTIVITY THAT FOLLOWS

ACTIVITY
WHAT do you do and WHY do you think you do it?

You have specific behaviors, activities, rituals, and ways of doing things that have become important to you and affect your daily levels of satisfaction or dissatisfaction. You probably learned these habits from a parent or caregiver, a teacher or a mentor. What matters here is for you to become aware that everyone else has a number of habits that are more important to them than others, as well.

Do you recognize any of the following examples as being especially important to you?

- Making your bed every morning
- Doing the breakfast dishes before leaving for work
- Doing laundry on Saturday morning
- Checking email first thing at work
- Calling your parents every week
- Exercising a certain number of times per week
- Eating specific foods at holidays
- Sending birthday cards without fail
- Organizing the calendar around certain special days
- Working in a particular way to assure productivity
- Making lists before you go to bed
- Updating a gratitude journal at the end of every day
- Reviewing the ups and downs of the day

The purpose of the next activity is Self-Assessment.

In the following three steps, you will discover some of your specific behaviors and characteristics. You can take inventory for yourself, or, of course, for anyone else you may have in mind as you go through this course. This activity requires you to set aside judgment and create a list, much like a shopping list for the grocery store.

This list is just for you, and you do not have to share it with anyone.

Be factual. Don't judge. AND: Save this inventory for future use in the following units.

Step 1 - Take an Inventory of What You Do

Create three vertical columns with plenty of room to write your responses. In the first column, answer the following questions as matter-of-factly as you can.

- What behaviors, activities, or rituals are parts of your daily/weekly routine? (e.g. I take a morning walk, I shower after breakfast, I review email before I leave for work, I write a positive daily affirmation to set the tone for my day, I make my bed, I take my own lunch to work).
- Which of those are high priority for you?
- Which of those create a certain feeling of urgency? Things that you feel you MUST do to maintain calm and focus; otherwise, if you don't do them, you feel disoriented or uneasy.

Step 2 - Honestly Determine WHY You Think You Do WHAT You Do

Look back at the list you created. In the second column, next to each item in the first column, write the first reason that comes to mind for why you do it. If there is more than one reason why this behavior matters to you, write it down as well. Quickly work your way through your list until you have at least one reason for why you do each item.

Step 3 - How long have you been performing this behavior, activity, or ritual?

For the last part of this activity, ask yourself the question: "How many months/years/decades of my life have I been doing this?" Or: "How old was I when I began doing this?" Write down the first answer that comes to mind in the third column, and don't overthink.

Now you have a multi-columned inventory that's easy to refer back to, like the example below:

What You Do	Why You Do It	How Long You've Done It
Make my bed	I like a neat room	Since age 11
Take a walk	For clarity and fitness	Since 1998

Note: You will refer back to this list in future units, so keep it safe and accessible.

What I Do	Why I Do It	How Long

QUOTE FROM THE *GUIDED JOURNAL*

Day

62

A Healthy Sense of Self is what it takes to fully Be Your Self.

When you are yourself
you stand a much better chance
to stay free
from the many problems that plague us in our day
and age:

relationship problems,
problems with learning (children/young adults),
problems with addiction,

or with money,
self-sabotage,
fear of failure,
(domestic-) violence,
suicide,
and even
acts of war!

RECAP

In this unit we asked you to catalog, with as much objectivity as you could, WHAT you do in the course of a day or as a matter of habit or routine. The habits and behaviors we learned in childhood travel forward with us as we develop in either healthy or unhealthy ways. Becoming self-aware of this is especially useful for people who feel they are not completely in charge of their actions and behavior.

QUIZ

Here are three questions to verify (for yourself) whether you have a good understanding of the concepts of Unit 1:

1. How can you solve many of your issues?

_____

_____

_____

_____

_____

2. Why is it important to be completely honest with yourself?

_____

_____

_____

_____

_____

3. Why is it important to know the reason for WHY you do WHAT you do?

_____

_____

_____

_____

REFLECTIVE QUESTIONS

Here are three reflective questions to deepen your understanding of

Unit 1 as it relates to your Self:

_____

_____

_____

_____

1. After cataloging some of your daily activities, which one do you have the most emotion attached to?

_____

_____

_____

_____

2. How do you feel when you encounter obstacles when performing activities that are important to you?

_____

_____

_____

_____

3. Do you have certain reactions when you are unable to perform an activity in your normal manner? How would you prefer to react?

_____

_____

_____

_____

LOOKING AHEAD

Are you surviving or are you thriving? That is the idea we explore in the next unit. If you aren't living an autonomous life, does that count as truly thriving? And what exactly do early experiences with your caregivers have to do with how you conduct yourself as an adult? You may remember having a great childhood and have concluded that it is just *you* who is unable to live up to certain conditions, but what was operating in the background?

NOTES

_____

_____

_____

_____

_____

_____

_____

_____

_____

_____

_____

_____

_____

_____

_____

Unit 2
Whose life is it, anyway?

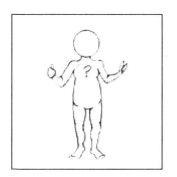

Another purpose of this course is to help you get your life back. You might *think* you are living your own life, but how can you be sure of that?

Unit 2 offers insight into the difference in the quality of the lives of people who have a Healthy

Sense of Self compared to those who are eternally struggling to find themselves—to find out who they are—of those who suffer from an inner emptiness they fill with achievements, which causes their lives to become one big performance.

The central question in this unit is "Whose life is it, anyway?" Getting in touch with your own opinions, choices, preferences, and feelings needs to be facilitated and supported early and often in life, when you are young. If that doesn't take place, your life may end up being about living up to expectations of others and meeting specific (often times self-imposed) conditions that you perceive to be of life or death importance.

What are these expectations and conditions? They are conditions you assumed you had to meet in order to get your caregiver's approval when you were very young.

BENEFITS

Some benefits of Restoring your Sense of Self are:

- Comfortable facing your Self, more Self-accepting
- More likely to have clear preferences, tastes, and opinions, and be able to stand up for them

- Know what you want
- Overall higher quality of life

NEW SoS TERMS
Natural Sense of Self (NatSoS)/ Lack of Sense of Self (LoSoS)

Natural Sense of Self

The subconscious sense—developed normally in childhood—of being alive as a "real," definite person, who has an unconditional right to exist as you are, regardless of what others think, feel, or say about you.

Two groups of people

Have you ever met someone who seems genuinely at ease in their person? They seem to take risks and try new things with confidence; they deal with the natural level of fear that comes with new experiences much better than some others, who seem to freeze when faced with the same fear. These people say what's on their minds and do not feel reluctance to disagree with their parents, or later with their superiors. They clearly feel they have a right to be seen and heard by others; they intrinsically know they have the right to BE.

When there are no obstacles for you to develop naturally as a person, from early childhood on, you test and question the rules set *for* you and later *by* you. But even the ability to discern the value of those rules is rooted in the capacity to think independently. A person with a Healthy Sense of Self develops that skill; the person with a Lack of Sense of Self becomes dependent (in their thinking) on the outcome of conditions that (they believe) need to be fulfilled in order to get other people's approval.

Humanity could almost be divided into two groups of people: one, as just described, that has a Healthy Sense of Self, and the other that doesn't.

Lack of (Natural) Sense of Self (LoSoS)

Characteristic of people who never developed a natural, ongoing inner knowing that he or she feels truly alive as a "real," independent human being.

Are people pleasers really serving others?

There are people who stand out for an entirely different set of reasons. They seem *not* to have the capacity to do, or even to know, what they want. They look constantly to others for direction, ideas, and a standard to live by. They seek to avoid conflict, and though it looks like they are serving others, it is purely because of the absence of any conviction in themselves. It could be said, therefore, that rather than serving others, this attitude is self-serving. In the end, though, it really is at the expense of the opportunity to live their very own lives. This unhealthy situation takes its toll in many ways.

Controlling behavior

What can be misleading about this type of person? While it appears they have a strict set of norms they live by, if you look closely, those norms are products of a need to control their environment. They depend on the outcome of their activities and need things to be "just so"!

What did it take for them to become a person who lives life in this way? Whose opinion or approval counts most to them?

GUIDING QUESTIONS

Here are a few questions you may elaborate on either in your thinking, by speaking aloud (perhaps into a recorder), or in writing—whatever way you prefer.

Was there any room in your childhood for you to simply BE who you were at the time?

_____

_____

_____

_____

_____

_____

What memories have shaped your becoming who you are now?

_____

_____

_____

_____

When unpleasant memories surface, what effect do they have on you? How do you deal with them?

_____

_____

_____

_____

READING SELECTIONS *FROM HEALTHY SENSE OF SELF* – UNIT 2

Excerpts from Chapter 2

WHOSE LIFE IS IT, ANYWAY?

Self and Sense of Self

Before we can understand how we come to fail to develop our Sense of Self (SoS) and make an effort to regain it, we must take a step backward and define what the Self is and what it is that makes up the Self. We also need to take a closer look at what is meant by "sensing" in "Sense of Self" and what Self and Sensing the Self are not.

What Is the Self?

The Sense of Self Method proclaims that strengthening or, if needed, restoring your Sense of Self is a key to reducing and/or eliminating many aspects of human suffering. So what does this Method consider the "Self" to be?

The **Self** has been an object of study and wonder for philosophers and psychologists for many centuries. If you want to learn how traditional psychology views the Self I refer you to the many good books about this subject. It is neither the purpose nor the scope of this Method to review and incorporate other relevant theories on this subject. The reader can compare or relate the underlying approach to what is already out there if he or she so wishes.

In the SoS Method, the Self is considered to be composed of six layers that, each in their own specific way, need to undergo a healthy and adequate development so each can contribute to a fully functioning healthy unit of interactive layers that we can compare the Self to. Note that the ability to sense this Self itself also depends on the opportunity or circumstances a person (child) has to effectively have those layers unfold their potential and do what they need to do at the time that it is meant to happen.

Even though the process of developing a healthy natural SoS is meant to go smoothly, all too often people encounter obstacles that hinder this process from taking place in a healthy, natural way. Please note that this is a crucial moment in the development of the young person and exactly the reason why a situation can be created in which the person identifies with other ways of giving his or her psyche a structure.

Lack of Sensing, Not a Lack of Self

Before moving forward, I want to make it very clear that it is not a deficiency of Self that I consider the root cause of many ailments and dysfunctions in our daily lives but an inability to Sense the Self. The development of the ability to Sense the Self was obstructed during the crucial moments in a child's upbringing.

I wish it were possible to quantitatively measure the degree to which a person is (or is not) tuned into his or her Self. We could then measure when and to what degree that process is actively working in each individual person. I wish that we could attach numbers to the degree to which each person experiences their Self. We might be surprised to learn how greatly those numbers would vary, with the low numbers being found in many more people than we would think, specifically in people who have many problems in life.

The Natural SoS

A Natural Sense of Self (NatSoS) is the most rudimentary and natural awareness of our own Being and of our be-ing alive. In this fortunate situation, every layer of the Self is healthy and, having developed correctly, as we grew, performs satisfactorily according to its intended function. A Natural SoS is an abiding, unshakeable, subconscious awareness — the sensation of being an autonomous human being, ultimately independent of others, especially from our parent or primary caregiver(s). Having a Natural SoS does not refer only to physical independence, which obviously does not happen until adulthood, but also and most importantly to psycho-emotional independence. Having a Natural SoS can be considered the anchor of a person's be-ing. It is our ultimate inner home, or more exactly, it is who, what, and where we mean when saying or thinking "I" and "me." It is the place from where we act and are motivated.

This type of SoS feels natural to us, by which I mean unquestioned, unquestionable, foundational, basic, and intrinsic, because it has always been with us and it has grown with us as we age. It is so natural to us that we do not even need to become consciously aware of it, that is, to refer to it by words, by name, or by labeling it because of its steady, ongoing presence.

What people with a Natural SoS have in common is one important, automatic characteristic: the ability to be at rest. A Natural SoS provides us with the one and only safe haven we can expect to have in life: No matter what we do or what we do not like about ourselves a person with a Natural SoS can always rely on the security of the "I am" bedrock it provides. Being rooted within us, it cannot be affected by superficial, or surface, matters. With a Natural SoS, internal peace and confidence are the rulers of our being even when the world around us is in turmoil and chaos.

A Natural SoS makes us aware that we are a distinct "someone" different from other "someones." It allows us to fully be ourselves and enjoy being alive as who we are. It opens us to experience joy and personal satisfaction and allows us to be free to experience what we truly feel, to relate to others authentically without unhealthy filters, and to feel compassion. A natural Sense of Self is a blessing that permits us to focus on the content of our lives and "get things done" (without being distracted by an eternal search for the Self).

Self-Esteem Requires a Sense of Self

The use of the word self-esteem is popular these days, as low self-esteem is also often used as the root cause of many problems, but self-esteem and Sense of Self are not the same. According to Merriam-Webster's Dictionary, self-esteem is "confidence and satisfaction in one's self; self- respect." In the SoS Method, the concept of self-esteem follows this definition, that is, confidence that is based on the opinions of others and/or the judgments of others that we have internalized. In this context, self-esteem is indeed built on events and things outside of our being—a healthy self-validation or pride in one's achievements or performances— and is not part of the profound Self.

So if we want to compare self-esteem, and its counterpart, self-loathing, to our SoS concept we just need to agree with the following truth: Before we esteem or loathe something, we must be aware that it exists. We must sense it. In other words, we cannot have low or high or whatever self- esteem if we do not sense our Self in the first place.

Therefore, self-esteem is something that people with a Natural SoS can experience, but those without it cannot because they are unable to connect with the Self.

PROCEED TO THE ACTIVITY THAT FOLLOWS

ACTIVITY
Who was/is important in your life—starting when?

Each of us has stories about who most influenced us in our early years: teachers who made an impact or mentors who guided us when we first started working. There are people you meet throughout your life who make a strong impression, either immediately or over time, and who leave you with a new way of seeing or doing things. Sometimes the influence is positive and sometimes it is not.

Regardless, these people are important to you, and who you become is influenced by their presence in your life.

For this activity, *quickly* draft a list of the people who are (or have been) important to you and for how long they have influenced your life. No evaluation or analysis, just the simple details of who it is/was, and for how long. They might or might not still be living, their influence may have been present since birth or only recent, a longtime connection or a new one; the common denominators are that they are IMPORTANT and MEMORABLE to you.

Here is an example:

– My great grandmother, since the day I was born.
– My birth mother, since I was reunited with her at thirty-four years old. My daughter, since her birth thirteen years ago.
– My high school English teacher, since age fourteen.

This list will be used for a future activity that deepens your awareness of WHAT you do and WHY you do it.

_____

_____

_____

_____

_____

_____

_____

_____

_____

_____

_____

_____

_____

_____

QUOTE FROM THE *GUIDED JOURNAL*

DAY
49

How do you get access to your very own life?

By freeing your Self from the addiction to a
Substitute Sense of Self

There is a dependency on
"Feeling-good-about-yourself"
because
it functions as a Substitute Sense of Self.
It is based on
APPROVAL.

Restore your Sense of Self!
Be in and with your body
Think for yourself
Know WHY you do WHAT you do!

That gives you freedom from the addiction to
approval…

Now you can be true to your Self.

RECAP

Being born doesn't come with a guarantee that you get to live your own life.

You either got the very early support you needed to develop a Natural Sense of Self, or you ended up with a Lack of Sense of Self. In this Unit, you learned to make that distinction and are now on your way to discover in which of the two groups you fit: Do you have a Healthy Sense of Self or a Lack of Sense of Self? To enable you to answer that question you were asked to make an inventory of early influences in your life.

QUIZ

Here are three questions to verify (for yourself) whether you have a good understanding of the concepts of Unit 2:

1. How can a Sense of Self be Natural?

_____

_____

_____

_____

2. What is a Lack of SoS and what effect does it have on a person's life?

_____

_____

_____

_____

3. Is pleasing your parent/caregiver always a good thing?

_____

_____

_____

_____

_____

REFLECTIVE QUESTIONS

Here are three reflective questions to deepen your understanding of Unit 2 as it relates to your Self:

1. Now that you have learned what a Natural Sense of Self is, can you think of someone you know who has one?

_____

_____

_____

_____

2. Are you a "people pleaser"? How does this affect your life?

_____

_____

_____

_____

3. Whose approval is most important to you? Why?

_____

_____

_____

_____

_____

LOOKING AHEAD

The next unit investigates what lies at the root of developing a Healthy Sense of Self and looks at where the developmental process can go wrong. We will discuss certain survival mechanisms that are innate to children, and how the decisions made during that time continue to be important throughout the rest of your life. You will find out how parents and caregivers have the crucial function of reflecting back to you the message that you are a person who is real, by truly seeing and hearing you. You will have the opportunity to think back and assess your own experiences and how they have impacted you as a person.

NOTES

Unit 3

Your past shapes your present. Is your present good enough to shape your future?

You are born to live your very own life but that is easier said than done. Observing your Self heightens awareness and sets the stage for making the decision that it is time to do things differently.

In Unit 2, we asked you to consider the relevance of how your caregivers related to you during your earliest years and how that translated into whether you developed a Healthy Sense of Self or a Lack of Sense of Self. Were you being seen, heard, and related to as a human being who was potentially equal to your parents? These early experiences set the stage for the development of a *Healthy* Sense of Self or they pull your attention and focus in a different direction.

What exactly did you learn from your caregiver(s) before you even acquired language? And after that?

Unfortunately, many children are essentially forced to focus on their parent's needs and wants rather than developing a sense of their Self. When healthy **Mirroring** (see below) doesn't occur, there is a greater chance that these children become puppets in the lives of their parents.

If this describes your childhood, you were left with an undeveloped sense of your Self—you were set up to fail to grow your own psychological backbone. Throughout your life, you remain driven to do what your caregivers tell you, verbally or non-verbally, as you need their approval to survive (see below: Early Childhood Survival Strategy).

Taking this into consideration, ask yourself: What elements of your past are affecting your present? What might this do to your future if nothing changes?

BENEFITS

Some benefits of having a Healthy Sense of Self are:

- More common sense, more realistic, more "real"
- Less controlling of others and of situations
- More inner peace

NEW SoS TERMS
Mirroring / Early Childhood Survival Strategy

Mirroring

The subtle, mutually subconscious process by which the primary caretaker conveys to his or her child a sense of either being a means to fulfill the caretaker's emotional needs or being a "real" and unique person—this sense functioned as a mirror for the child during infancy and was accepted as the truth of who he or she is.

"Do you see me? Do you see me for who I am?"

If you could talk from the moment you were born, this would probably be the very first question you would ask your mother and father. Most likely you spent nine comfortable months in your mother's womb feeling connected and safe; then came the day you were born.

The way your parents related to you

Note that in the SoS Method it is not about your parents loving you or not. It is about whether or not your parents were really seeing you and relating to you as a potentially autonomous and independent human being. Did they consider you to be an individual, living as your own person, after you were born—a person who was separate from themselves? Or did they treat you as a sort of extension of themselves, as a pawn in their own games?

Unconditional acceptance of you as YOU

Maybe your caregivers took excellent care of your basic needs at first, but were they (over time) truly able to cut the umbilical cord and relate to you as your own person? Did they respect you enough to encourage you to become YOU? Were they glad you were a part of the family? Was there a basic recognition/acknowledgment of you and your "you-ness" as you grew up?

Or did you feel that you had become a burden because they were so busy with themselves? Could they handle you being a noisy, happy, cranky, messy child as you explored your new world? Did you feel that your caregiver(s) wanted you around regardless of your mood, or was their love and attention conditional? OR, did you feel you had to find a way to conform to required conditions and behave in certain ways so that you got a sense of being tolerated and experienced as acceptable? Were you (desperately) looking for that sense of being *allowed to be* in your mom or dad's facial expressions, the tone of their voice, their patience with you?

Ideally, your parents gave you true attention and you felt seen and heard as you grew into your own Self. That's what the HySoS Method calls "healthy, adequate mirroring."

Early Childhood Survival Strategy (ECSS)

Conclusions drawn subconsciously by infants/toddlers/ children about how to get their needs met when they do not feel acknowledged as separate (unique) beings by their caretakers. This process becomes the foundation for an unhealthy way of experiencing the self.

When your basic needs are not met, a Survival System kicks in.

From the outside, it might have looked as if your parents were doing the right thing, but in their minds and hearts they were busy living for some other, possibly unknown, goal—they had an issue from their own childhood that they needed to work out or felt they had something to prove. They were mentally and/or emotionally already preoccupied with something else. They were not available to truly *see* you for the little person in development you were.

Infants, toddlers, and children have a sense for that missing aspect, as it is crucial for them to be acknowledged; the growing child has to find out what to do to get their needs met one way or another. The natural inclination to do so plus the resulting conclusions are what is called the ECSS.

Approval versus acknowledgment

Being acknowledged as a separate and unique person is a basic human need during early development, so Mirroring matters greatly. In your battle to feel acknowledged, you develop skills to get as close to that feeling as you can. This takes the place of learning life skills and developing a sense of your Self.

You focus on what to do and how to be (ECSS) in order to get the signs (through approval) of being seen and taken into account by your caregiver, all the while mixing up acknowledgment with approval.

Please make sure you answer the following question:

How far did you have to go to get your most basic needs met early in life?

_____

_____

_____

_____

GUIDING QUESTIONS

What needs attention and healing in your present life?

_____

_____

_____

What areas of life cause you pain?

_____

_____

_____

With whom do you have unfinished business and what is the unfinished business?

_____

_____

_____

Who would you be if your childhood need for acknowledgment had been fully met?

_____

_____

_____

READING SELECTIONS FROM *HEALTHY SENSE OF SELF* – UNIT 3
Excerpts from Chapter 3

YOUR PAST SHAPES YOUR PRESENT. IS YOUR PRESENT GOOD ENOUGH TO SHAPE YOUR FUTURE?

Environmental Input: The Developmental Decider a Strict Sequence

When a Sense of Self (SoS) starts to develop in a person, and that starts right at birth, it follows a particular pattern with particular input at particular times. Children who do not get what they need at the right time grow up locked into compensations that are self-destructive and that cause all kinds of suffering and problems.

Before we explore the natural, healthy process of how a person ought to grow up and compare it with what happens when that process is distorted in one or more ways, here are some thoughts about growth processes in nature.

Every infant, seedling, or animal goes through a formation process. Even after it has sprouted or been born, its anatomical and functional systems are still forming. This process follows a strict sequence that is pretty much predetermined by nature and, as a whole, it is also being influenced by the interaction between nature and nurture.

The genes of each living being are its "nature" aspect. The circumstances in which the being exists are its "nurture" aspect. These two influence each other, such that genes or circumstances may reinforce the growth and development of a plant or animal in one direction or another. Some processes need to take place before others can. If some bit of a living being's physiology does not develop fully and appropriately at its given time—its "critical period"—the clock marches on anyway. When this critical time passes, the being is abnormal in some way, unable to live up to its full (initial) potential.

As it is with plants and animals, so it is for people. So much of who we are as people, and how our lives unfold, is initiated in our childhood. So let us take a brief look at what happens in childhood.

Humans do not stop developing after they are born. Development follows certain natural rules and certain patterns; for example, we crawl before we walk; we walk before we run; we babble before we talk. Another important but often overlooked rule is that certain kinds of input are required at certain times in the sequence for the development to occur as it is meant to. If the right input happens at the right time in the sequence, a child's development is normal and healthy. If a child does not experience the correct conditions, it will grow in an unnatural and defective manner. It might be alive, but it is distorted and weak, and it struggles to function.

For example, an infant, during this process of formation—which can be specific and unique to a particular critical period in the sequence—needs various kinds of physical environmental inputs, such as adequate food, water, and warmth, as well as specific interpersonal, psychological, and emotional input. To understand fully the necessity of these inputs, it is necessary to realize that both physical and psychological inputs affect both body and mind.

The natural in Natural SoS means a person has a SoS that has developed at the natural time, in an adequate way, and in the natural order that the development of a human being requires. It indicates the development has been "normal"—that the human consciousness has been able to do what it is programmed to do, without encountering obstructions or **Hindrances** *in facilitating the maturation process. If the various required inputs are not present or provided at the appropriate time, the development of a Natural SoS cannot take place, and the result is a person with a warped SoS.*

When developed in a distorted manner, we often need others to support us.

A SoS is not something we are born with or that we develop automatically and inevitably, no matter what. We do have an inborn drive to develop it, but unless certain kinds of experiences (feedback) are provided and processed in infancy and early childhood, a SoS won't develop naturally and normally.

A core sense of an independently existing me-ness is part of normal, healthy human development, and our psychological development programs that into us. Normal development requires a specific attitude from the primary caregiver toward the child; this attitude needs to communicate certain information to the child about his or her "being." This specific attitude needs to provide to the child the building blocks for the development of a Healthy Sense of Self, and is called Mirroring.

PROCEED TO THE ACTIVITY THAT FOLLOWS

ACTIVITY
What is the state of your Sense of Self?

Now that you have begun to take an inventory of what you do and why you think you do it, as well as who has been important to you or has had a strong influence in your life, it's time to check on the state of your Sense of Self.

Follow the directions to take this quick self-assessment worksheet designed to give you an initial idea of what group you might belong to (HySoS/LoSoS):

- Do you have a Natural Sense of Self?
- Or did your Early Childhood Survival Strategy mean that you are geared towards gaining approval, that unhealthy surrogate for feeling like a "real" person.
- Do you lean toward a Lack of Sense of Self?
- Have you begun restoring your Sense of Self?
- Or do you already have a Restored Sense of Self?

Have you ever heard the expression: "peeling back the layers of the onion"? It refers to learning more about something or someone by peeling back the layers. That is the point of this next activity.

Circle or highlight the statements you identify with as being generally true for you. Move quickly through the lists and accept your first answer of "yes" or "no" without stopping to reconsider or doubt yourself, and then immediately move on to the next. Calculate the total number of statements you said yes to at the end of each list.

After tallying up the number of statements in each section that you identified with, you will be in the position to determine if you are a person with a Healthy SoS *or* if you lean toward a Lack of SoS *or* perhaps you are showing signs of a Restored SoS!

Wherever you are at, know that with awareness comes the ability to heal yourself!

Perhaps you have a Healthy Sense of Self?

o   I believe I received adequate supportive parenting for growing a Natural Sense of Self.

o   I have the ability to focus on chosen actions or goals. o I do what I do only for the obvious and usual reasons. o I do not feel I have a Hidden Goal.

o   I have moments where I simply feel good about myself.

o   I understand everyday life has its ups and downs and that is all there is to it.

o   Overall, I am not easily hurt or excited.

o   My emotions are rooted in my Self.

o   I have energy available for happiness and joy.

o   I am comfortable with being by myself.

o   I see myself as living in the "Real Reality" and am able to focus on the things in front of me.

o   I am often very much present in the moment.

o   When I close my eyes, I experience inner sensations of balance.

o   I consider myself to be independent, and potentially interdependent with those close to me.

o   I can see others for who they are.

o   I have the ability to listen to others and actually hear them.

o   I am able to do what needs to be done or what I desire to do, taking into realistic account my own well-being, my potential, and/or my limitations.

o   I have a healthy sense of boundaries.

o   I normally sleep well.

o   Yes, I can get angry, but it's usually short-lived.

o   I generally manage stress well.

o   I am generally successful in my endeavors.

o   I am able to improvise.

o   I am comfortable making choices and committing to them.

o   I knows what I want and what I care about.

o   I know what my values are.

o   I have personal preferences and tastes that are not influenced by others.

o   I eat in moderation.

o   I do not eat because of stress.

o I have the healthy ability to let-go and leave things till tomorrow.

o I am generally even-tempered and emotionally balanced.

o I experience my body's center of gravity in my lower belly.

o I experience energy as being spread evenly throughout my body.

o I don't have car/motion sickness.

o I typically manage well in crowds.

o I generally feel balanced, because things don't affect the core of me.

o My emotions are related to my own individual personhood.

o I have the ability to attain and experience love and happiness.

o I take care of my body and generally have good posture and muscle tone.

o When accidents happen, they are experienced on a **Quality-of-Life level**.

TOTAL:_____

Or perhaps you lean toward a Lack of Sense of Self and therefore have a Substitute Sense of Self?

o My parent/caretaker was/is excessively focused on their own self (self-absorbed).

o My parent was unable to adequately mirror a Self to me as a child.

o My sense of safety or belonging is dependent on the outcome of my actions, my achievements, and of the degree to which I live up to expectations.

o I judge myself based on other people's opinions of me.

o I focus on fulfilling the requirements of Ego-References and Hidden Agendas so I can reach my one and only Hidden Goal of getting my caregiver to acknowledge me.

o My actions and behaviors are often indirectly motivated.

o I experience an excessive/obsessive need to reach the state of "Feel-good- about-self," and at times it feels like a matter of life or death.

o I experience emotional rollercoasters: excessive excitement and anxiety as well as deep valleys and depression.

o I have a need for (rewarding) highs.

o I rely on the opinions of others for feelings of belonging or group-identity.

o I am an idealist and believe that Utopia is possible (not in touch with reality).

o I sometimes feel like I'm living in a trance.

o When I close my eyes my inner sensations are often chaotic and confused.

o I feel out of touch with myself.

o I still use my childhood strategies for getting my needs met as an adult.

o I see and hear others only when they are useful for my self-serving (usually Hidden) goals.

o I use others as pawns or Vehicles to fulfill Ego-References.

o I see key figures from my past in others all the time and they trigger certain reactions in me.

o I have some compulsive and obsessive behaviors.

o I feel that there is no room for failure.

o I often lie awake at night (subconsciously) obsessing about finding the "Feel-good-about-self" state or keeping the one I reached during the day. (Since this is not happening consciously, it is just indicative here of what could be at play when you lie awake at night and have no clue why.)

o I experience panic attacks, migraines, anxiety, depression, and/or thoughts of suicide.

o I have issues with unreasonable anger, rage, and/or violence.

o Chronic unmanageable stress.

o I am prone to chronic and widespread failure in my endeavors.

o I focus on obtaining my Hidden Goal instead of on the usual outcome of my actions. (This too is happening beneath the conscious level of awareness and should be seen as an indication of what could be at play if you experience frenzy or abnormal upset when trying to reach your goal).

o I can be extremely controlling of myself, others, and circumstances.

o I am often inflexible.

o I have no improvisational skills.

o I am easily angered by unanticipated turns of events.

o I am often in flight or fight mode, which causes erratic behavior and bad decisions.

o I am uncomfortable making choices.

o I have difficulty committing to a choice after I've made it.

o My tastes and preferences are not personally authentic; they are based on the tastes and preferences of my parent.

o I am prone to eating problems such as anorexia, bulimia, or overeating.

o Eating helps me feel grounded.

o I eat to numb my emotions or to alleviate stress.

o There is simply never enough time to get everything done.

o I have very little ability to let go of unfinished assignments and consider myself to be a workaholic.

o I am often over-excited, driven by the wrong Motivation, frenzied, anxious, overly sensitive, and/or high-strung.

o I experience feeling non-existent, wretched, flat, depressed.

o My center of gravity feels as if it is outside of my body.

o I am prone to car/motion sickness or vertigo.

o I have a fear of crowds or feel like my Self is dissolving when I am in crowds.

o I am easily aggravated, nervous, upset, and/or offended because everything is perceived as a threat.

o I get feel physically anxious upon perceiving (Substitute Sense of Self–oriented) success.

o I believe that love and happiness are not within reach for me.

o I have a great deal of tension in my muscles that leads to pain in my neck, back, and shoulders.

o I am accident-prone.

TOTAL:_____

Or do you have a (partially) Restored Sense of Self?

o I have more ability to focus on things than I used to.

o I am increasingly content-oriented and my actions are increasingly done for the obvious and usual reasons.

o My actions produce much better results than they did in the past.

o My anxiety is decreasing due to the lessening need to reach the "Feel-good-about-self" state.

o I am increasingly able to simply feel good about myself on a Quality-of-Life level.

o During usual daily life, I feel that nothing existential is at stake.

o My mood much more balanced.

o I am in touch with my authentic inclinations, tastes, and preferences.

o I am increasingly comfortable being by myself.

o I no longer experience a desperate need for belonging, and my relationships with others are less strained as a result.

o I now see myself as a "Realist apprentice" as I am increasingly aware of own situation and willing to work on improving it.

o I am aware that theoretical dream solutions are of no importance in "Real Reality."

o I have a growing awareness of what the world is really like and I pay more attention to current events than I did in the past.

o When I close my eyes my vision field is much quieter and my bodily sensations feel calmer.

o Overall, I feel increasingly more connected to myself and others.

o I am often present in the moment.

o I have an increasing ability to focus on actual real life.

o I am developing the ability to focus on my genuine personal wellbeing.

o I can tell the difference between my Hidden Goal and my authentic goals.

o I am becoming the Master of my life and can resist the influence of others with greater frequency.

o I am ready for team work and cooperative activity.

o I see and hear others for who they are.

o I know that accepting my Self leads to the acceptance of others.

o I am letting go of controlling behavior.

o I am learning to distinguish dedication from compulsion.

o I now experience more dedication and less compulsion.

o I sleep much better, knowing that I don't have to earn my Self by fulfilling specific conditions.

o I no longer experience the **Fear of Annihilation**.

o I rarely experience excessive fear, anxiety, and/or panic attacks, as compared to the past.

o I am aware of the value of my own life.

o My feelings of desperation have been (mostly) eliminated.

o I experience anger on a healthy Quality-of-Life level.

o I generally manage stress well.

o I focus on real things and on what I want my life's purpose to be instead of on my Hidden Goal.

o I am no longer prone to self-sabotage.

o I feel visible to others.

o I am no longer attached to outcomes and my need for control is greatly reduced.

o I no longer feel as if I am in flight or fight mode during everyday situations.

o I have a growing ability to make decisions and commit to them.

o I have discovered what I truly care about, want, and value.

o I am able to set priorities and boundaries and gauge my own potential.

o I have developed authentic personal tastes and preferences, sensed as aspects of my Self.

o I don't turn to food to help me feel ground.

o Achievements, actions, and events are experienced on a Quality-of-Life level.

o I am much calmer and have gotten more in touch with my authentic temperament.

o I have less tension than I used to.

o I feel grounded within myself when traveling, and I rarely or never experience motion sickness.

o I feel grounded within myself when in crowds.

o I am more emotionally balanced.

o I am a lot less sensitive when it comes to normal daily life.

o I no longer experience those waves of physical anxiety.

o I do not experience over-excitement.

o I believe that love and happiness are within reach for me, but I didn't always feel this way.

o I am much more relaxed than I was in the past.

o I can let my heart lead without interference from my head!

o I am less accident prone because my behavior is more deliberate.

TOTAL:_____

So now that you have begun to self-assess where your Sense of Self is anchored, sit back and take a moment to clear your mind. Before you start to pass judgment on the present state of your SoS, do this instead:

1. Take three deep cleansing breaths and acknowledge that you dove into this activity and were simply honest about your experiences.

2. Remind yourself that you have done what it takes to get by in the world and the family you were born into.

3. Be gentle and compassionate with yourself instead of critical of the 'you' that you are.

4. Take on the role of an observer and see what strengths you developed as a child—acknowledge yourself for being intelligent in doing so.

5. Begin to ask yourself: What no longer serves me? Am I willing to let that belief or behavior or strategy go so that I may live my own life more fully?

As with the previous exercises of Lessons One and Two, this material and inventory you have collected is going to be used for a deeper dive into YOU. Healing yourself and restoring a Sense of Self begins with awareness of what is—and now you have a clear list of what is true for you at this moment.

Wherever you are, know that with awareness comes the ability to heal yourself!

You have to peel back the layers of your Sense of Self to find out what kind it is.

QUOTE FROM THE *GUIDED JOURNAL*

DAY

21

Having Ego-References*
is a condition that is based on your
Early Childhood Survival Strategy:

While observing your caregiver
when you were a toddler,
you wondered:
"How do I have to be or what do I have to do
so he or she gives me something
that looks like
love?"

*The concept Ego-References will be explained in Unit 5

RECAP

The early way you were related to by your primary caregivers affects how you relate to yourself on a subconscious level and is (in part) responsible for what you make of yourself during your lifetime. Unless you take initiative to develop and implement a different way of relating to yourself—by reconditioning yourself, or by becoming your own parent—you might stay trapped in this web of early experiences. Breaking free starts with seeing what really happened. The information in this unit is meant to provide you with some labels to help you understand what went on in your childhood.

QUIZ

Here are three questions to verify (for yourself) whether you have a good understanding of the concepts in Unit 3:

1. Describe in a few words what an Early Childhood Survival Strategy is.

2. What is Mirroring and why does it matter?

_____

_____

_____

_____

3. How are Mirroring and Early Childhood Survival Strategy linked to one another?

_____

_____

_____

_____

REFLECTIVE QUESTIONS

Here are three reflective questions to deepen your understanding of Unit 3 as it relates to your Self:

1. What do you think some of your own Early Childhood Survival Strategies were?

_____

_____

_____

_____

2. What are some of the specific things you had to do to fulfill your caretaker's (emotional) needs?

_____

_____

_____

_____

3. What is something you can do to get in touch with your Self?

_____

_____

_____

_____

LOOKING AHEAD

Now that you have gone through the HySoS checklist and gotten an idea of which kind of Sense of Self you have, we will introduce in Unit 4 two categories of motivation identified by the SoS Method: Direct Motivation and Indirect Motivation. The type of Motivation at play in your life is primarily determined by the type of SoS you have—a

Healthy SoS or a Lack of SoS—and these are determined by the quality of Mirroring that you received in early childhood. Please be prepared to go deeper into (your) Motivation-and into WHY you do WHAT you do!

NOTES

_____

_____

_____

_____

_____

_____

_____

_____

_____

_____

_____

_____

_____

_____

_____

_____

_____

Unit 4
"Thinks" are seldom what they seem

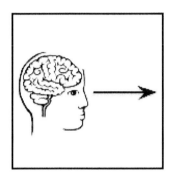

Your personal preferences and tastes are formed based on your Sense of Self, but a Lack of Sense of Self can lead to an addiction to approval and overshadow your true desires. When you spend your life catering to the needs and wants of others rather than your own, the motivations behind your actions and behaviors may become twisted.

To understand your motivations, you require awareness of what is happening in your subconscious mind—just beneath the surface of your conscious mind, there is always something more going on than what is visible and apparent. In this lesson you are invited to consider which of the two main types of motivation underlies your actions and behaviors. Can you distinguish between the times when your Motivation is Direct or Indirect? Can you identify any situations where it is not quite clear?

BENEFITS

Here are three more benefits of having a Healthy Sense of Self:

- Better aligned with your personal blueprint
- Less uncontrollable behaviors (e.g., temper tantrums)
- Better equipped to deal with criticism; less over-reactive

NEW SoS TERMS
Motivation / Direct Motivation / Indirect Motivation

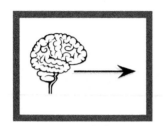

Motivation

In general, motivation is what creates an incentive or urge to do or avoid something. Motivation is the drive that determines behavior.

What is Motivation?

As the definition states: Motivation is an urge to do or avoid something generated by a need or want.

Two types of Motivation

There are two categories of motivation identified by the SoS Method: Direct Motivation and Indirect Motivation. Discerning which kind of Motivation is operating in the background of your various behaviors is the key to self-knowledge, to healing a Lack of Sense of Self, and to gaining a Restored Sense of Self.

Direct or Indirect Motivation for something you do (or don't do) is primarily determined by the type of SoS you have: a Healthy SoS or a Lack of SoS. And that is determined by the quality of Mirroring you received in early childhood.

Examples of motivation in general:

- Most parents are motivated to care for their children by the love and responsibility they feel for them.
- Finding a job is generally motivated by wanting to make money so you can provide for yourself (and your family).
- A person is motivated to eat to alleviate the sensation of hunger.

Direct Motivation

Motivation that is ordinary, simple, and based in the present.

Direct Motivation is characteristic of people whose innate need to feel recognized as a real person was adequately met in early childhood. People with a Healthy Sense of Self have no specific unmet needs that would give rise to Indirect Motivation. They do things for the sake of the things themselves; they take action for the immediate and obvious result, or simply for the joy of the experience. Their behavior is based on who they are as a person, or on an overt and obvious goal.

Here are a few examples of Direct Motivation:

- When parents are (directly) motivated to care for their children, it is because they love and value their children and genuinely want to see them thrive.
- A clown acts funny because it is his job to make people laugh.
- You get up in the morning because you are awake and want to start your day.
- I wash my car because I want it to be nice and shiny.

Indirect Motivation

The motive for doing or avoiding something is not what it appears to be; instead, the motive is to accomplish your Hidden Agenda, and ultimately your Hidden Goal, which leads to a temporary emotional state that is the substitute for a lasting sense of being a real person.

Where does Indirect Motivation come from?

You know by now that Indirect Motivation is rooted in a childhood Mirroring deficiency that leads to a Lack of Sense of Self. The Lack of Sense of Self leaves an inner void that you try to fill with (parental) approval.

What does it aim at?

You do things or behave in ways that you hope will lead to this approval, which makes you (mistakenly) feel acknowledged as a real person. As it was said earlier: a child easily mistakes approval for acknowledgment.

Most Indirect Motivation involves a need to perform something to perfection. Performing well becomes a matter of life and death because the ability to feel like a *real* person who is accepted by others depends on it. As such, it can become compulsive and determine the course of your life entirely. *Instead of living your (own) life, you have become a performer of your life!*

Nothing is what it seems to be.

When your life is ruled by Indirect Motivation, it means that you have been conditioned to develop subconscious drives to be and act in ways that give you the closest approximation to acknowledgment: approval. That means there are more complex stories going on behind your actions and behaviors than might be apparent.

**If your underlying drive is to satisfy the need to gain
the approval of others, then that is the signal that
you are operating with a Lack of Sense of Self.**

In later lessons you will see how this is the root of a lot of human suffering.

**However, please be informed that your suffering
can be greatly reduced
by learning how to shift your
Motivation from Indirect to Direct.**

Here are a few examples of Indirect Motivation:

- Parents who have a need to be considered good parents by others, or who are looking to get the approval of their own parents, are Indirectly Motivated to care for their children.
- If you get out of bed in the morning because your inner parent is saying you're lazy, or if you feel like an utter failure if your dog isn't fed exactly on schedule, chances are that you're Indirectly Motivated.

GUIDING QUESTIONS

Identify an activity or behavior that you suspect you perform for Indirect Motivation. Monitor yourself closely over time to see if you can discover a pattern of thought or behavior that you weren't previously (consciously) aware of.

What is the activity you will monitor?

_____

_____

_____

_____

With this new awareness, do you think you can make a different choice based on what YOU yourself are thinking in that particular situation?

_____

_____

_____

_____

Can you turn off your automatic pilot and implement a new decision or course of action that is more in line with who YOU are? What do you hope will change?

_____

_____

_____

_____

READING SELECTIONS FROM *HEALTHY SENSE OF SELF* – UNIT 4

Excerpts from Chapter 6

"THINKS" ARE SELDOM WHAT THEY SEEM" MOTIVATION AND THE SUBSTITUTE SENSE OF SELF

Introduction and Overview to Motivation

This Method states that understanding and purifying your motivation is the key to developing and maintaining health and a reasonable degree of happiness. In other words, understanding your motivation is a crucial first step if you want to tackle the task of healing yourself from the dependency on a Substitute Sense of Self (Substitute SoS) and move toward Restoring your Sense of Self (SoS).

If you understand your motivations, you have a key to understanding yourself. Why do we do what we do, or avoid doing some things, often at all costs? If we understand what we are actually after, we come closer to seeing the whole picture of ourselves. By figuring out what our ultimate goals are, we get to know ourselves thoroughly and learn what we are all about. Self-knowledge is power! Knowing ourselves fully will enable us to make smart decisions that also benefit others.

Discovering Our Motivations Is Not Easy

In order to be useful, our discovering of our motivations, of this key, requires total honesty with ourselves. That might seem easy enough. It isn't. Finding out the truth about our deepest motivations is not obvious, nor simple or easy.It is a challenge because we human beings are masters at denial. We might be ready to admit that we sometimes deceive others by pretending we are closer to our ideal self than we are. Try on the shocking admission that you might be going out of your way to deceive yourself, even for a whole lifetime! Yet that is what many of us are doing!

How Do Our Motivations Develop?

This Method presents a new and holistic approach to the understanding of the human condition and the potential changes that can be made. Our point of departure is that the body, mind, and emotions are continuously in communication with each other, which then results in the way each person is what he or she is in the world right now.

Here's one way to look at that. You are born with certain qualities and characteristics of who you are on a soul level. If there are few obstacles to your developing a healthy mind and body, then your life circumstances are allowing you to live up to that potential.

But what happens though if there are too many obstacles, and your development, as it could naturally go, is blocked and distorted by some life circumstances? (This actually happens to many of us.) Then nature seeks ways in which your body, mind, and emotions can compensate for the lack-of-growth and/or health-promoting life circumstances.

How does motivation develop differently in those two cases? In a healthy situation, we know motivations by describing the obvious reason why we do something. In the unhealthy situation, motivations become more convoluted. We develop complex patterns of subconscious motivations in nature's attempt to compensate for our thwarted natural development.

Labeling Motivation as Direct and Indirect

In this section, you will learn how unhealthy motivations develop. First please make sure you understand how a healthy, Natural SoS develops (see Chapter 3). We see how a child's motivation is formed by its circumstances and environment. Based on that understanding we will discover that motivations can be divided into direct (healthy) and indirect (unhealthy, the result of thwarted development), and you will learn how this comes in turn from and contributes to a healthy or unhealthy SoS. When you will be able to see the connection between a healthy NatSoS and Direct Motivation and how Indirect Motivation points to a Substitute SoS you are on your way to healing!

What Is Motivation?

In this Method, Motivation is generated by the reasons or reasoning we have (consciously or subconsciously) for doing or avoiding doing things. Motivation is the force that drives us to act and the incentive for our behavior. It either refers to a reasoning or force that moves us to act and that is the incentive for our behavior toward a goal that is experienced as desired and that aims at satisfaction ("fun"). But the drive to do or not do something can also be much stronger and reflect our needs or perceived needs for survival ("need"). In this Method, motivation refers more generally to the reasons, either conscious or subconscious, we have for doing or not doing things. It provides us with an agenda of doing what we are motivated to do and provides us the goal of accomplishing whatever we are motivated to do. This distinction of motivation as being fun- or need-oriented will be addressed later in the chapter.

Why Is Knowing Our Motives Important?

Questioning my motivations and coming up with true, sincere answers was the key to getting insights when working through my own self- knowledge toward my healing. Once the insights were there, the potential for healing was created. "What exactly drives me to do what I do, or avoid so strongly what I don't want to do? What are the real reasons for my choices and behaviors?"

I remember the many instances during the time I worked as a professional bassoonist when I was unable to stop practicing or preparing my reeds. It felt as if my life literally depended on the quality of my performance. In hindsight I can see why I was so compulsive in my preparations for a concert—I could not afford for others to think I was a bad musician and go home with that devastating feeling of having failed to perform well. It felt as if my spirit would evaporate until the next time when I would do well.

"Thinks Are Seldom What They Seem"

Consider these examples of differing motivations, which are hard to spot for the common observer.

> *Here we have two mothers and each take their child to a music school. Even though to an observer these two people are "doing the same thing," their motives might be totally different. One might be motivated to develop her child's talent and help the child be happy in the activities involved in that development. The other might be motivated to have a child who is a good musician because it reflects well on her as a parent.*

The outcome of the experience would therefore be different for all involved. The first mother and child would probably find satisfaction and mutual enjoyment. The second mother and child would probably have stress, fights, tensions, and mutual dislike. And the child might not only rebel at the activities, but feel disempowered, manipulated, resentful, and inauthentic. So why did I get started in music?

> *Two mothers are complimenting their children after a test at school. It looks as if they are doing the same thing. But their motives could be different, and the effect of the compliment could be different in each case, too.*

The first mother might be motivated by unconditional love, and recognition of the child's intrinsic worth, so she is supporting her child's self-image by calling her capable and loved no matter the test results. The effect of the compliment would be smiles on both faces, a deepening of their bond, and better mental health for the child. The second mother might be giving the child approval, which the child knows is only because of a good test result, a good performance. The child would be glad, but already worried about future failures. The mother might be getting an emotional rush from having a child who appears intelligent to the world, thus reflecting well on her own intelligence, which she isn't sure is high enough to get her own mother's approval. The mother's motive is to have the child do well on future tests.

For the second mother it isn't really about the child, and a nagging fear of future failure lurks for the child as well as for the mother through the child. The child is a pawn in the mother's game. The child senses she needs to perform well in order to get "good vibes" from the mother; the mother depends on the child for her "Feeling-good-about-self" (Fgas) state.

PROCEED TO THE ACTIVITY THAT FOLLOWS

FOUR ACTIVITIES
Peeling back the layers of your own Motivation

In Unit One you created a list of things you do and why you *think* you do them. Please take out that list and review it. This unit is entitled *"Thinks" are seldom what they seem…* and that is the focal point for the following activity.

Think again about your motivation for an activity or behavior on the list you made in Unit One. Of course, there's what you may think your motivation is for doing something. But is there also another motivation hidden from your conscious awareness? Be absolutely honest with yourself. Remember that honesty is essential for what you are trying to establish: a Restored SoS.

One of the clues that can tell you whether a motivation is Indirect is that you experience intense feelings, such as fear, compulsiveness, rage, frenzy, hurry, and anxiety when you are not accomplishing your goal. There could also, or instead, be sensations like butterflies in your stomach, a rapid heartbeat, shallow breathing, sweating, etc., especially in moments when you think you are going to be successful. All of these can be indicators that there is more happening within you than the obvious, surface motivation.

The question you may want to ask yourself now: Is the intensity of the emotions you experience justified by the actual event?

Activity Exercise #1
Consider your motivation for being on time to a class.

Some of the possible Direct Motivations to be on time are simply:

1. You feel mentally prepared for whatever it is you want to do there.
2. You want to be respectful of the teacher and other students.
3. You don't want to create a disturbance or distraction.
4. You don't want to miss the beginning of the lesson.
5. You want to have fun socializing before class begins.

A few of the possible signs of Indirect Motivation for being on time are:

1. You get overly bent out of shape when traffic, kids, or pets cause delays.
2. You feel like there is a whole lot at stake when you're running late but you don't really know what it is.
3. You panic/melt down if you run out of gas.
4. You get anxious/panicky/upset when you are unable to find a parking space.
5. You are constantly checking the clock while driving—or the opposite: you do not want to look at it for fear of having to conclude that you are not going be on time, and start freaking out.

Questions to ponder for Activity Exercise #1
Think of a recent event or appointment.
1. What layers of your motivation can you unpeel?

_____

_____

_____

2. Were you on time? If not, did you feel anxious about being late?

_____

_____

_____

3. Did the appointment or event go as planned?

_____

_____

_____

_____

4. How did you feel afterwards?

_____

_____

_____

Activity Exercise #2
Consider what your motivation could be for not expressing your opinions.

Direct Motivations might include:

1. You are talking to a policeman who is writing you a ticket.
2. It's not appropriate for the social or professional situation you are in.
3. You know you want to leave in five minutes and don't have time to deal with a complex conversation.
4. You do not have any particular opinions to share on the given topic.
5. You know your opinion differs from the person you're talking with and will bring about an unpleasant situation that you want to avoid for obvious, practical reasons.

Indirect Motivations might be:

1. You are scared to share your thoughts/opinions because you feel anxious about the possibility of someone disagreeing with you or challenging of your idea.
2. You have the need to come across as smart, so you can't afford to risk being seen as stupid.
3. You have an intense—even desperate—need to belong, so you do not want to ruin your chances by saying something that might alienate you.

4. You want to draw attention to your choice not to share, because it makes you feel that you are better than others—that you don't stoop to their level.

5. You need to protect a state of "Feeling-good-about-self"* that you have gained by pleasing someone; you are afraid of losing that state by saying something others might respond negatively to, and make you feel bad about yourself.

*The SoS term "Feel-good-about-self" will be discussed in Unit 6. For now please check the Glossary for a short definition.

Questions to ponder for Activity Exercise 2: Remember a time when you could have shared an opinion or experience with others, but you didn't.
1. Why did you hold back?

_____

_____

_____

_____

2. What feelings were involved?

_____

_____

_____

_____

3. What layers of motivation can you discover?

_____

_____

_____

_____

Activity Exercise #3
Consider possible motivations for someone not asking for what they want or need.

1. What are at least three Direct Motivations for this not-asking that you can imagine someone might have?

_____

_____

_____

_____

2. What are at least three Indirect Motivations for this not-asking that you can imagine someone might have?

_____

_____

_____

_____

Activity Exercise #4
Looking again at your list of What/Why from Unit 1, answer the following questions:

1. Which items have sometimes caused you to experience anxiety, panic, or frenzy?

_____

_____

_____

_____

2. Which items have caused you to start sweating or notice that your heart races or skips a beat?

_____

_____

_____

_____

3. Which items give you an uneasy sensation in your stomach?

_____

_____

_____

_____

4. What is it that you think/feel is ultimately at stake for you in each item on your list (the underlying reason that motivates you)?

_____

_____

_____

5. As you review your list, contemplate whether your motivation for each item is really as obvious as you first thought it was. What insights have you gotten so far?

_____

_____

_____

_____

QUOTE FROM THE *GUIDED JOURNAL*

DAY
60

Motivation Check

Questioning your motivation
is a very powerful tool for
getting to know your Self.

Understanding where you come from
is necessary
to be able to change the direction
toward
where you wish to go.

RECAP

Questioning your motivation is not only powerful but also necessary for you to begin to understand whether you are living from a Lack of Sense of Self or a Healthy Sense of Self. A life lived with Direct Motivation is ideal, and knowing WHY you do WHAT you do is crucial. When you have the ability to see when you are acting out of Indirect Motivation, you can begin to recondition your Self to work from motivations you choose based on what is truly your very own desire, need, or want. That is how you begin to Restore a Healthy Sense of your Self.

QUIZ

Here are three questions to verify (for yourself) whether you have a good understanding of the concepts in Unit 4:

1. What is Motivation?

_____

_____

_____

2. Describe the difference between Direct and Indirect Motivation.

_____

_____

_____

3. How does Indirect Motivation relate to your Sense of Self?

_____

_____

_____

REFLECTIVE QUESTIONS

Here are three reflective questions to deepen your understanding of Unit 4 as it relates to your Self:

1. What are some activities or behaviors that you are Directly Motivated to do? Think about why you have a healthy relationship with those activities or behaviors.

_____

_____

_____

_____

2. What are the most common emotions or sensations you experience when you are Indirectly Motivated? Think about what the root cause of these feelings could be.

_____

_____

_____

3. Which action or behavior that you are Indirectly Motivated to perform do you most want to change?

_____

_____

_____

_____

LOOKING AHEAD

Even though, at first glance, your motivation seems straightforward, the "thinks" you think may be rooted in and directed toward a subconscious agenda and your ultimate "WHY" of *WHY you do what you do*, and not so much with WHAT you are doing.

Some of the items on the list you created in Unit 1 might have become things you identify with—some may even be fully integrated into the very essence of the person you are. In the next unit we will address why these things play such a dominant role in your life and what is behind that.

NOTES

Unit 5

Are you using your life to prove that you are okay?

One of the objectives of the SoS Course is to help you identify certain unfavorable processes that take place on a subconscious level. These processes are not self-serving, but they can lie at the root of many of your life choices without you being aware of it. Labeling these processes allows you to first recognize them and then to see a pattern emerge. This leaves you in a position to find out exactly what it is that drives you to do or avoid certain things. After you've confirmed what these ultimate motivators are, you have the option to make different choices—of your own free will—if change is needed or desired.

Unit 5 introduces two of these labels. One is called *Ego-References* and the other is *Vehicles*. They point to patterns of behavior that have not been consciously identified by you as coming from Indirect Motivation; possibly patterns that can keep you preoccupied without you even being aware of it.

BENEFITS

Some benefits of gaining a Healthy Sense of Self are:

- Feeling comfortable in your own skin
- Ability to self-realize and live life to the fullest
- A better balance of head and heart; genuine and integrated feelings

NEW SoS TERMS
Ego-References / Vehicles

Ego-References

Subconsciously accepted requirements to feel and behave in certain ways and achieve certain results in order to feel approved of, as a substitute for feeling like a "real" person.

Ego-References are self-imposed conditions or requirements that are based on your attempts, as a very young child, to be acknowledged and truly seen and related to by your caregivers—to be accepted as a potentially independent person, with a right to live as yourself. Decisions about how you should behave and what you should do to please your parent are what later became your Early Childhood Survival Strategy, which is stored in your subconscious (see Unit 3).

Over time, living up to these (self-imposed) conditions becomes compulsive, because they serve your need to get approval in lieu of acknowledgment. In reality, the only result you get from living up to these conditions is the limited satisfaction of *temporary* approval.

Where does the word come from?

"Ego" is another word for the identity you *refer* to when you say "I." So you could say it is a kind of "I-reference," for those who lack the real "I-experience." Ego-References typically form the foundation for the Self-experience of a person with Indirect Motivation, and thus with a lack of Sense of Self.

Here are a few examples of Ego-References:

- I have to stand out from the crowd
- I must never complain about anything to anyone.
- I always have to be on time.
- I always have to sleep well.
- I always have to be in good spirits when I get up in the morning.
- I have to be slender and look good.

These are but a few possible Ego-References a person can adopt. There are too many to name, and they will be different for each person depending on the preferences of that child's early caregivers and each individual's personal circumstances.

Vehicle

An activity or behavior used to display the performance of specific skills or character traits rather than being used for the obvious, ordinary goal of the action or behavior. The performance is ultimately aimed at getting approval.

Ego-References are the self-imposed requirements aimed at convincing your caregiver that you can be who they want you to be or do what they want you to do. And these Ego-References need a carrier action or behavior to demonstrate the specific aspect you want to show off to get that certain outcome (approval). That carrier action or behavior is what is referred to as the Vehicle. Vehicles are the means you use to achieve the desired outcome of an Ego-Reference. They carry the Ego-Reference until it is realized, and if the Ego-Reference was successful, approval is experienced (temporarily).

Because approval is temporary, you are continuously looking for opportunities for your Vehicles to perform or demonstrate that you can "do it" or "be it" in any given moment. In fact, great fear—even terror—can be experienced when you are not able to function fully, which consequently prohibits you from being able to succeed at an Ego-Reference; for example, by not sleeping, by being sick, or by not being prepared for a performance or task.

Each Ego-Reference can have a variety of possible Vehicles and employ different ones at different times.

The following are examples of situations that are opportunities for the use of a Vehicle to display an Ego-Reference.

- As a Vehicle to display the Ego-Reference that you are able to "not be angry all the time," contrary to what you perceive your caregivers think of you, you may use a situation in which you are swallowing your anger or upset when wronged.
- As a Vehicle for the Ego-Reference of showing that "you are not average" and that you are able "to stand out from the crowd," you may use any situation to be the first one to ask/answer questions or volunteer to do an activity, even if you are uncomfortable with it.

- A Vehicle for the Ego-Reference of showing that "I am good enough to live up to her conditions," can lead you to the situation of always ending up choosing difficult people to work with.
- As a Vehicle for the Ego-Reference "being on time" every time you are going to an appointment or event that requires timely arrival can be used. But note that you are doing the effort not for the right reason!
- As a Vehicle for the Ego-Reference of showing that "I am in good spirits" you can use specific tasks that allow you to show off that you are in good spirits, for example bringing flowers for someone, even if you don't see the point yourself, dressing up nicely even if you don't feel like it. You could get in touch with your true preferences in these situations if you could ask your Self—but the problem is you can't.
- As a Vehicle for the Ego-Reference of demonstrating that "I am not selfish" you may use specific actions or behaviors to demonstrate being helpful (expecting immediate approval and validation in return), whenever the opportunity arises.

These examples of Vehicles could refer to actions done for simple and obvious reasons, which would make them Directly Motivated. However, if you sense a compulsive need to perform them, you might have found a symptom of Indirect Motivation.

It is this sense of compulsion together with extreme amounts of stress that indicates these actions or behaviors are being used as Vehicles to temporarily satisfy an Ego-Reference.

One very important point about Ego-References is that they are rarely performed to the degree of perfection that would ordinarily happen if the task were done for healthy reasons. Because so much is perceived to be at stake in doing them well, the amount of stress and anxiety is extraordinarily high, and paradoxically, this interferes with the quality of the performance!

Ego-References come forth from conclusions made in early childhood and over time they formed your Early Childhood Survival Strategy. EgoRefs all have to do with the perception of needing to improve yourself, but not for your own sake! They are based on subconscious conclusions you made in the past (as a child), but can still be operating, in your present adult life.

Vehicles are actions or behaviors that you display—that come up during specific events, or circumstances—not because of the obvious goal, but because you want to show off your improvements of particular characteristics (Ego-References) or behaviors that you then hope will gain you approval, initially from your caregiver. This is what Indirect Motivation is all about.

Although Vehicles are (also) tasks and situations that are part of everyday life, on a subconscious level you use them to demonstrate that **you can do it** or **you can be it**.

A Vehicle then is an action or behavior that is chosen (subconsciously) as a specific way to perform one of your Ego-References.

An example: If your Ego-Reference is "to be on time (this time!)" and the situation to *show that you can do this* is your doctor's appointment, your doctor's appointment is the Vehicle.

Reiteration and conclusion

From the time you are born, you watch what goes on around you and pick up clues about what it takes to survive and to be seen and approved of by your caregivers. If you do not get the positive acknowledgment required for developing a Natural Sense of Self, your need of getting approval (in place of that acknowledgment) can grow to the point of desperation.

Possibly, even before you acquire language, you realize what it takes to get by in your family systems. When you sense your developmental needs are not being met in a healthy way, you make sure that you get them met in a different way. Certain behaviors, thusly chosen, later become part of your identity. When you are unable to develop a (healthy) sense of your Self, you adopt ways of behaving to gain acceptance from the people *you believe* you need approval from (ECSS).

But there is a difference between truly living one's life for the experience of it, and wasting the precious gift of life trying to prove that you are not as bad as you perceive. Identifying that difference is crucial, as it may give you your life back.

Try to discover, in yourself, specific ways of doing or being that cause you a lot of stress when you fail to do them just right. If you can discover one, chances are you have discovered one of your Ego- References.

Have you ever contemplated the possibility that you are not really living your own life? That your life could be a performance aimed at being seen in a particular way so you can feel accepted and approved of—to fill an inner void?

GUIDING QUESTIONS

List whatever it is that makes you feel good when others approve of what you are doing or how you are behaving.

_____

_____

_____

_____

_____

_____

What Vehicles do you use to perform each item on your list?

_____

_____

_____

_____

_____

_____

READING SELECTIONS FROM *HEALTHY SENSE OF SELF* – UNIT 5
Excerpts from Chapter 7

ARE YOU USING YOUR LIFE TO PROVE THAT YOU ARE OKAY?

Ego-References and Other Unhealthy Coping Mechanisms

So, indirect motivation is the immediate result of the dependency on our caregiver's approval that our understanding as a child takes for acknowledgment. Now that we have a sense of the difference between Direct and Indirect Motivation, let us shed a light on the pathway that is responsible for the motivation to be indirect.

So Ego-References refer to a set of required conditions to be performed at a high quality, and include specific behaviors and actions that we believe will satisfy the parent if we can improve our performance of them and that will get us the needed approval. They stem directly from the observations made in early childhood that are referred to in this work as the Early Childhood Survival Strategy (ECSS) (link).

Ego-References

The term Ego-Reference is central and unique to the Sense of Self (SoS) Method. It is a complex concept and part of the Substitute Sense of Self (Substitute SoS)–oriented System.

Ego-Reference as a whole has everything to do with referring to the Substitute Sense of Self, mistaken for the real (Healthy) SoS.

Each Ego-Reference, when worked on, is solely geared to win approval while soothing the fear for the perceived ever-present threat of (link) Annihilation that is lurking. Ego-References are grown into solid, unchangeable strategies. You have to think of them as less dense items, with an energy that is still not hardened into, what it becomes in later days, the compulsion a person can't remove from his or her path because it has become part of him or her. So in general when we speak of Ego- References the child has already grown into an adult.

The specific desired behaviors are meant to result in the person receiving the right "vibes" from his or her caregiver. For example, a person may think: "I have to finish this work today," not so much because the work needs to be finished—which would be

Direct Motivation for finishing the work—but because by finishing it early, I anticipate a sense of approval that will lead to me "Feeling-good-about-Myself"—which is the real motive for finishing the work.

Conditions That Become Ego-References

Which characteristics or behaviors become Ego-References depend on a person's individual specific circumstances. What the young child discovers when trying to adjust to the caregiver's demanding behavior or to the caregiver's responses to its own behaviors determines what Ego- Reference the person will develop. Each individual child discovers different behaviors (to do or refrain from) that evoke approval from his or her particular primary caregiver. Thus, each child develops actions and behaviors unique to itself and its situation, although there most likely are common patterns. It would be interesting to identify those by researching them more in depth. Chosen Ego-References might also have to do with the child's own specific temperament and inclinations and be colored by the particular conditions and requirements the child senses the caregiver is imposing on him or her. They can be, but are not necessarily, the caregiver's own Ego-References.

For example, whenever Erica, who had a hard time falling asleep, overslept, her aunt (who had raised her from when she was little) looked at her in a manner that said, "Why do you do this to me?" She would look at Erica with the look of an abused dog, which made Erica feel very guilty. It is not hard to fathom that Erica's Ego-Reference became "sleeping well." "I need to sleep well in order to get my aunt's friendship and approval, which would feel for her as if she was getting the keys to the castle." (This is a metaphor for her being allowed into her aunt's environment while feeling included.)

Similarly, when Erica was sick or feeling under the weather and had to stay home from school, her aunt silently resented the situation, because it would give her extra trouble. It would be a Hindrance on her way to having a clean house and everything taken care of, which would give her the desired Fgas state. Another interesting detail is that Erica's aunt did not allow herself to be sick either. Being sick was something the parents of Erica's aunt despised as well. It possibly was even an Ego-Reference to Erica's grandparents. No wonder Erica developed the inner command to make sure she was OK at all times, which would lead her to pretend she was fine, even when feeling under the weather, lousy, or nervous.

Ego-References and Vehicles

As discussed in the preceding chapter, the term Vehicle is used to indicate an action, activity, or behavior that serves as a carrier for and an opportunity to work on an Ego-Reference. The action that functions as a Vehicle has two functions: It brings about an overt result and it serves to realize a person's Hidden Agenda, which is a positive outcome of an Ego- Reference. A person's focus is only indirectly on the overt goal; the person's real intent is to attain the Hidden Goal and/or the Fgas state, feeding his or her Substitute SoS.

Here are some examples of behaviors used as Vehicles: household- or job- related requirements, paying a visit to someone, sending a card to someone, helping someone in any way, pursuing a certain education, educating children a certain way, going places, washing your car, being on time, and having a relationship partner, among others.

Examples of Ego-References

Remember that Ego-References are held subconsciously. Considerable introspection may be required to discover that you hold the belief— accepted in early childhood— that you desperately need to fulfill these conditions and requirements. We can think of Ego-References as self- imposed conditions but we need to be always aware that this was the best that could have been done. It was a second best option. Note that Ego-References are rules with unrealistic demands of "always"—there is no allowance for circumstances. Holding on to Ego-References degrades these peoples' quality of life and makes them the slave of fulfilling the conditions.

To get a better feel for what aspects of a person's life can become an Ego- Reference, here is a list of the ones I had.

- *As a mother, my family has to be positive and have a positive atmosphere at all times.*
- *I need to be in shape physically, emotionally, and psychologically so that I am always OK.*
- *I need to sleep well, be fit, be in a good mood, and look well- rested.*
- *I need to know what I want.*
- *I need to be on time.*
- *I have to have my act together.*
- *I need to achieve something in life, make something of myself.*
- *I need to stay away from getting angry, upset, irritated, or even annoyed.*
- *I need to avoid conflicts at all costs.*
- *I should never have or create problems for myself or anyone else.*
- *I have to make sure that I do not become sick or am not feeling well because it is not appreciated.*
- *I need to do things differently from other people and find a sense of being special.*

- *I need to be different from what and who I naturally am; I cannot just be who I naturally am.*
- *I have to stand out from the crowd.*
- *As a mother, I need to spend enough time with my children and husband.*
- *As a person, I must achieve great things in the world.*
- *As a homemaker, I have to have my house clean and well organized.*
- *As a spouse, I have to be in a good mood and never be angry.*
- *I must not complain.*
- *I have to be successful and admired.*

When I visited my mother in the last decade of her life (I was in my fifties), I would not enter her house without bringing some flowers or a little gift. I never thought of actually making her a bit happy; I did it to get approval. (Ego-Reference: "not being selfish.") I had to keep up with my sister who gave her so many presents and flowers. I had to keep up so much that there was no room left for any spontaneity.

Other times, I felt I had to take her on a few trips to change the impression that I was leading a selfish life. My sister did it, so I also had to do it so I would not lose points. But due to the lack of predictability in my sleeping pattern I was unable to offer that as generously for it tied directly to another Ego-Reference, one that already was a hot item during my visits to my mother: I had to sleep well to actually be able to plan to take her out.

PROCEED TO THE ACTIVITY THAT FOLLOWS

ACTIVITY
What Vehicles might be supporting your Ego-References?

For this activity, pull up that list you created in Unit 1. You will be looking again at the things you do, and thinking more deeply about them this time. The goal of this activity is to discover: What is the absolute bottom line for WHY you do WHAT you do? In other words, what is your root Motivation?

This unit is entitled "**Are you using your life to prove that you are okay?**" This is the focal point for the following activity.

While working on this task, keep in mind that Indirect Motivation is prompted by Ego-References, and that there needs to be a means—a Vehicle—to allow the Ego-Reference to be carried out in real time.

Step 1: Choose one item from your list and think about it further. Answer the following questions:

What do you think your true motivation is?

_____

_____

_____

_____

_____

What do you perceive to be at stake?

_____

_____

_____

_____

_____

Step 2: As you review your list, contemplate what possible Ego- References and Vehicles might be at work.

Which items have become so important that they must be done at all costs?

_____

_____

_____

_____

_____

Step 3: Pick an item from your list that you feel highly motivated to do often and perform well. Imagine failing at it or giving it up altogether.

What feelings surface when you imagine either scenario?

_____

_____

_____

_____

What are you really trying to achieve by doing that activity or behavior as well as you feel you must?

_____

_____

_____

_____

What is in it for you?

_____

_____

_____

_____

What do you think the consequences of failure or giving it up would be?

_____

_____

_____

_____

QUOTE FROM THE *GUIDED JOURNAL*

Day
36

For us who want to be seen and heard

When you have a Lack of Sense of Self

chances are
you are just running around
trying to live up to all the conditions you have
imposed on yourself...

They're based on

how your caregiver (parent) needed you to be
because you thought

that by being just more "so"
or doing more of "that"
your caregiver might look at you in a more
positive way and could even "see" you.

RECAP

This unit was about understanding what the HySoS Method refers to as Ego-References and the Vehicles used to accomplish them. You were asked to identify which characteristics and behaviors you have that could possibly function as an EgoRef or a Vehicle and which might add suffering and anxiety to your life.

QUIZ

Here are three questions to verify (for yourself) whether you have a good understanding of the concepts in Unit 5:

1. How was the SoS term "Ego-Reference" born?

_____

_____

_____

_____

_____

_____

2. Are Vehicles real cars? What are they used for?

_____

_____

_____

_____

_____

3. What important concept of the SoS Method are Ego-References and Vehicles closely related to?

_____

_____

_____

_____

_____

_____

REFLECTIVE QUESTIONS

Here are three reflective questions to deepen your understanding of Unit 5 as it relates to your Self:

_____

_____

_____

_____

1. Which of your EgoRefs causes you the most anxiety?

_____

_____

_____

_____

2. What are some of the Vehicles you use to carry out this particular EgoRef?

_____

_____

_____

_____

3. How do you think it would affect you if you no longer lived with this EgoRef?

_____

_____

_____

_____

LOOKING AHEAD

In the next unit, we will investigate what else might be going on when you try to achieve Ego-References through Vehicles. What is it that drives you to crave approval? We will look at the concept of "Feel-good-about-self" and find out that, as simple as it sounds, there is a whole lot more to it.

NOTES

_____

_____

_____

_____

_____

_____

_____

_____

_____

_____

_____

_____

_____

_____

_____

_____

Unit 6
The need to "Feel-good-about-self" can be compulsive

Every person has the right to live life as their Self, and this course was intentionally designed to enable you to reset your mental and emotional "operating system." The process of reconditioning allows you to do the following three things:

1. Find the driving force behind your current behavior and acknowledge how it is influencing your current reality. In other words, find an answer to the question: "Where, exactly, do the incentives to live up to certain rules and conditions originate?"

2. Verify and, if necessary, acknowledge that the rules you apply to your life and the conditions you use as criteria to reach the "Feel- good-about-self" state are not (always) based on your own values or opinions.

3. Recondition your Self to *think with your own mind* and *feel with your own heart*; let your own voice and self-expression break through.

This course offers insight into the processes that may be at play within yourself. That way you can get to know yourself better and consciously make changes that stick!

Some of us have been condemned to a life of addiction to approval, which results in the constant need to work frantically to gain the desired outcome of activities and performances. It may feel as if your life depends on it. If this applies to you, *and you are eager to turn that situation into a healthier one*, it is necessary to recognize and take an inventory of the ways in which YOU aim to get your needs met.

Unit 6 introduces a few processes that contribute to the subconscious drama at play in those with a Lack of SoS. These processes are not obvious, but if you pay attention you can recognize their presence by identifying certain symptoms:

- Continuous self-evaluation and/or self-judgment
- The ever-present motivation to "try harder" and succeed at all cost
- Difficulty sensing what is realistic and/or practical

We will show you how to shift from being (solely) focused on reaching your Hidden Goal (approval and "Feeling-good-about-self") to focusing on what YOU want your life to be like, based on your own conscious decisions.

The graph below illustrates the sequence of the concepts we have dealt with so far.

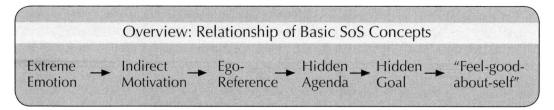

Overview: Relationship of Basic SoS Concepts

Extreme Emotion → Indirect Motivation → Ego-Reference → Hidden Agenda → Hidden Goal → "Feel-good-about-self"

Understanding and identifying these particular processes within yourself is necessary to overcoming them.

BENEFITS

Some benefits of gaining a Healthy Sense of Self are:

- Lower divorce rate
- Sense your own limitations, boundaries, potential, and talents
- Less violence and verbal abuse
- Less war

NEW SoS TERMS
Hidden Agenda / Hidden Goal / "Feel-good-about-self" (Fgas)

Hidden Agenda

A subconscious purpose that drives your actions or behavior, which is not the obvious, ordinary, expected purpose but the demonstration of the ability to perform an Ego-Reference to perfection, as a path to feel safe and on your way to achieving your Hidden Goal.

Your earliest experiences with your mother and father either put you in the fortunate position of learning life skills from them, or forced you to spend that time studying your caregivers to learn the behaviors that made it likely for you to get your needs met—being seen and accepted by them and feeling affirmed in your existence. This is what lies at the root of developing Direct or Indirect Motivation, (see Unit 4 for review).

An agenda is a list of things to be done. In general, your agenda behind doing or avoiding certain things coincides with the *usual result* of your action or behavior. Here is an example: "I clean the car *because I like my car to be nice and shiny*."

In many cases, you have an agenda attached to certain actions that is not so obvious: "I clean my dad's car *because I want to surprise him*."

The Hidden Agenda referred to in the SoS Method is comparable with the latter example, only it works on a more existential level. That is, if the goal of "cleaning my dad's car" is not only to surprise him, but *to gain approval, change his opinion about you from negative to positive, and make him truly see you*, which obviously, he has not been able to do so far.

Your Hidden Agenda is the real motive for your Ego-Reference (EgoRef); however, an EgoRef is not tangible, and you cannot work on or "perform" an EgoRef without having a carrier (Vehicle) for it (see Unit 5 for review).

The action or behavior that is the carrier for the EgoRef, is not done solely for the obvious motive, but is merely an excuse to perform the Ego-Reference.

In many instances the action or behavior that functions as the carrier for the EgoRef, including its *Hidden Agenda,* is something that needs to be done anyway:

"I need to keep track of my money." If being responsible with money is one of your EgoRefs, your Hidden Agenda will consist of doing it so well that, ideally, "my dad changes his opinion about me" and you glue that agenda onto the action that needs to be done anyway.

The behavior becomes a carrier, a Vehicle, for the EgoRef. It is not done for the sake of itself, but rather it is mainly done to reach your Hidden Agenda, which, in its turn, is meant to help realize your Hidden Goal (see explanation below).

The action is, therefore, likely to induce an excess amount of stress, causing you to feel that you need to track your money at all cost (before you can even begin to "Feel-good-about-yourself").

Another example: "I wash my car not because I want it to be clean but because tomorrow I will be visiting my parents. I know how they value a clean car; I need to do everything I can to get them to approve of me."

Even if you never succeed in permanently changing your caregiver's opinion about you, that vibe of approval makes you "Feel-good-about- self," which then functions as a virtual spine.

> When a Sense of Self was never developed, you generate
> these Hidden Agendas to help you achieve that state of
> "Feeling-good-about-yourself." In that case, your actions
> are not what they seem, but instead have become a
> performance that serves to get you approval.
> First from your caregivers, and then from the authority figures that
> have taken in their places throughout your life.

What is your priority then? You work to realize your Hidden Agenda, because realizing your Hidden Goal is perceived as a matter of life and death.

Living to serve the Hidden Goal means making sure that you do things perfectly, that you behave perfectly, so you are not rejected. Living like this can be seen as your way of making yourself feel relatively safe. It is a way that helps you counter the anxiety of feeling as if you are regarded as a "ghost with a body," a being who is present but who has no voice and no impact on your environment.

Hidden Goal

Your subconscious ultimate objective of getting the approval of your caregiver. This approval functions as an unhealthy substitute for feeling valued and related to (acknowledged) as a "real" person.

Note: This Hidden Goal is valid only when there is an emotional emergency and need for attention and approval, due to feeling as if you have not been seen and heard as a "real" person with your own voice. This condition makes you dependent on earning, over and over again, the approval and acceptance of those specific people whose approval you need to feel safe (Fgas). Primarily the people that should have facilitated and supported you in developing a sense of your own Self early in life.

When you were little, and as you grew up, watching, evaluating, and judging: What was going on between your parents and yourself (and perhaps your siblings)? Some part of you was smart enough to recognize what your caregiver really wanted you to do or to be.

What were they really after when they told you to do or avoid certain things? Were they really concerned about you or were they more self-concerned? Did they maybe want to fulfill their own Hidden Agendas and Goals?

Often, caregivers aren't even aware of their own Hidden Agendas, and while they might not have intended it, their agendas were adopted by you. All you wanted was their approval, so you did your best to give them what THEY needed, rather than paying attention to what YOU needed.

During your youth, you learned that this temporary sense of validation gained through approval made you feel that

you were allowed to be.

This feeling functioned as your virtual spine in the absence of your own Natural Sense of Self. Without internal support from a naturally developed virtual spine, you felt as if you were not like everybody else. You needed the confirmation of

"Yes, you're okay"

to make you feel safe. Getting that feeling then became your Hidden Goal, and it was experienced as being of life-or-death importance.

"Feel-good-about-self" (Fgas)

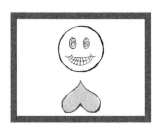

The temporary emotional state (or thought) of relative well-being and safety based on the absence of feeling compelled to produce certain results at all cost, which is gained from accomplishing what leads to approval and serves as an unhealthy substitute for a sincere sense of being alive as a real person.

Maybe you already know those fleeting moments of self-satisfaction don't feel as hearty or wholesome as they could. Do you feel you must repeatedly recreate those moments of temporary relief from the need to? Can you recognize the compulsion to keep a specific person feeling okay about you to, again, receive their approval or acknowledgement? That compulsion is driven by the need to "Feel-good-about-self," to prove that "I am okay."

"Feeling-good-about-self" is a subtle state experienced as a short period of relative safety and therefore makes you feel more relaxed.

It can also be thought of as a few moments of positive self-evaluation,
a "Thinking-good-about-self"
if you will.

It ranges from being excited about the outcome of an achievement or about a positive encounter with your parent, to feeling temporarily relief from the strain of having to perform your life to perfection. You were able to come close to living up to the high standards you set for your (inauthentic) self. Even as an adult, you imagine your parent would be pleased with you, or you may actually receive proof of their approval in real time.

The SoS term "Feel-good-about-self" refers to the moment of temporary respite from the anxiety and terror that are always present in a person with a lack of SoS. You are always anticipating that moment in which you will not be able to live up to your Ego-References, and consequently, will feel as if you do not have the right to exist.

The term "Feel-good-about-self" is meant to convey the absence of a negative, which feels relatively relaxed, but not so much happy or great, although that *can* be the case. "Feeling-good-about-self" is a moment in which the turbulence of working hard to get the desired result and the anxiety around not achieving that result is momentarily suspended.

The healthy alternative for "Feeling-good-about-self"
is feeling (truly) alive!

GUIDING QUESTIONS

Are there any activities that cause you to feel highly self-conscious?

_____

_____

_____

_____

Can you begin to envision a Hidden Goal in your life?

_____

_____

_____

_____

How often do you think a Hidden Agenda is attached to the things you do? (Never, sometimes, or all the time?)

_____

_____

_____

_____

READING SELECTIONS FROM *HEALTHY SENSE OF SELF* – UNIT 6
Excerpts from Chapter 5

THE NEED TO "FEEL-GOOD-ABOUT-SELF" CAN BE COMPULSIVE

Is "Feeling-good-about-self" a State, a Thought, or a Feeling?

In traditional psychology, thoughts are not to be confused with feelings. I learned this when going over the Sense of Self Method with Dr. Hal Dibner. The more I thought about that, the clearer it became to me how the "Feel-good-about-self" state was actually more a thinking good about oneself. It is basically a positive self-judgment that, based on the Substitute SoS–Oriented System criteria, is taken for feeling (sensing) the Self.

Over time during childhood, this feeling or state of judging oneself based on the fulfillment of certain conditions becomes a Substitute (unnatural, unhealthy) way of Sensing the Self. This state of judging oneself to have complied with the (self-)imposed conditions, and therefore being OK, functions as the ultimate goal in life and leads to compulsive behavior.

For those of us with a Substitute Sense of Self, life consists of mere moments of "Feeling-good-about-ourselves," like puddle jumping for children playing in the street, the dry pavement parts being the Fgas moments. The puddles need to be seen as the lapses of time spent on working hard to get the required positive outcomes and during which no Self is experienced. There is just an identification with the task at hand. Experiencing their Fgas state is their only reference to a self as it is their only way to avoid feeling annihilated. Because of this, they perceive reaching this state as a matter of life or death. Because this state results from actions or achievements that produce approval, they cannot stop trying to get the best-possible version of their action or achievement. This leads to "over" doing actions and achievements: They over-practice, overachieve, over-care, and so on.

The Role of the "Feel-good-about-self" State in the Substitute SoS–Oriented System

The Fgas state plays a crucial role in the structure of the psyche of a human being who has a Substitute Sense of Self. When I first set out to identify the importance it played in my life, I was still far from seeing the whole of this Method. I was not even aware that the only "feelings" I experienced were those related to my Hidden Goal and my Substitute SoS– Oriented System. The only feelings I was capable of were based on anxiety of not being able and/or in a position to make my Hidden Goal come true: being acknowledged as a valuable person in my mother's/parent's life and thereby getting a "virtual backbone." I experienced anger and desperation about possibly being thwarted or disabled in this process and I experienced fear that the Fgas state was always disappearing too fast.

These emotions were so violent and dominating that there was no room for anything that "stirs the heart"; no frequency was available on which this could occur. I always lived with the vague impression that something squashed my true (natural) range of feelings—that that something continuously squeezed out of my heart all the juices so I could not really feel something.

I thought that "Feeling-good-about-myself," which only happened when I fulfilled the conditions, was an exception, that it was really a feeling. Even working on fulfilling the conditions gave me an experience that simulated the Fgas state by anticipating it. So I was only relatively at ease when actively working on these conditions (Ego-

References). Anything else that needed to be dane or even anything else that was meant to be fun was experienced as anxiety provoking an d interfering with my actual goal.

PROCEED TO THE ACTIVITY THAT FOLLOWS

ACTIVITY

Now that we have added some terms, let's continue with the thread of conversation you started with yourself in Unit 5.

Step 4 (continued from Unit 5)
Try dropping an urge/activity/impulse from your Unit 1 list and watch yourself closely.

Note: We humans are highly skilled at coming up with justifications and excuses for the things we are addicted to, so please be aware of this and of the resistance you feel as you move through the activity.

What are the implications of consciously abstaining from fulfilling the conditions of your Ego-Reference and performing the task to perfection? Ask yourself if it really feels that terrible to not do these things to perfection. What are the implications for how you feel?

1. On a scale of one to ten, ten being the most uncomfortable, how uncomfortable is it for you?

_____

_____

_____

2. How long can you abstain from the behavior?

_____

_____

_____

_____

3. Can you gauge how it might have affected your quality of life?

_____

_____

_____

_____

Step 5
Part I: "Feeling-good-about-myself"
Ask yourself two questions. Here is #1:
What is your preferred way of getting to that "Feel-good-about-self" state? How are you trying to prove that you are *not* the way that (you perceive*) an authority figure in your life thinks you are? This person might be your parent or they might be your partner, friend, or your boss.

_____

_____

_____

_____

*I say: "perceive" because, even if you hear repeatedly "you are a failure," and to you it seems pretty obvious what that person thinks of you, you can never know for sure what someone is thinking. Often, you can only assume.

Whether or not the lines of communication are open between you and the authority figures in your life, you tend to interpret their behavior or verbal expressions and draw your own conclusions, regardless of their accuracy.

When you perceive that someone with authority does not really see you as the wonderful person you are AND you are in need of his or her approval (because you have a Lack of SoS), then the only thing in the world that counts is

to make them change their mind.

Proving you are worth their attention by doing things that they like to see you do is how you think you can achieve that.

Doing those things to perfection is your Hidden Agenda (as opposed to doing those things for the sake of the ordinary outcome) and changing their mind about you is your Hidden Goal. Only, that never happens and all you get is approval, which is nothing more than a fleeting moment of good vibes.

When people you value (and look up to)
are NOT ABLE to see you for who you are,
it might be
that they are too involved
with their own Hidden Agendas and Goals.

Here is question #2:

What is your Hidden Agenda when you engage in certain activities? What is your Hidden Goal?

Example: When Bart plays the piano and it goes fairly well, he gets to "Feel-good-about-himself." It makes him feel like a *real* musician, contrary to what he perceives his father, who idolizes musicians, thinks of him: "Ah, my son tries to be a musician, but I know that people in our family are just not musically talented. I so wish it were different and I could have been a great musician myself."

_____

_____

_____

_____

_____

_____

_____

_____

Step 5
Part II: What is your Hidden Agenda? What is your Hidden Goal?
So for yourself, could you create a formula, which would be something like:

When I *clean my house*, I go on doing it until I get to a
"Feel-good-about-self" state.
That happens when I *get every chore done to the standards set by my parents.*
My parent/caregiver used to think *that I was negligent or incompetent in my housekeeping*, which still hurts my feelings, and my self-respect suffers quite a bit because of it.
I realize that I am determined to prove that I can be *as neat as they want me to be.* I hope secretly that (someday) my parent will (finally) see me in a different light and acknowledge me for who I am. All I want is for them to appreciate me as *their valued and respected child.*

Replace the italicized text in the example above with facts from your own life:
When I

_____

_____

_____

_____

_____

I go on doing it until I get to a"Feel-good-about-self" state.

That happens when I

_____

_____

_____

_____

_____

My parent/caregiver used to think

_____

_____

_____

of me, which still hurts my feelings, and my self-respect suffers quite a bit because of it.

I realize that I am determined to prove that I can be/do.

_____

_____

_____

_____

I hope secretly that my parent will see me in a different light and acknowledge me for who I am. All I want is for them to appreciate me as

_____

_____

_____

_____

Understand that this outcome is a goal you might carry with you throughout your life. Until you gain their acknowledgment and respect, which is not likely to happen, you might play out this scenario in all kinds of relationships (family, friends, work).

_____

_____

_____

Step 6

Now that you are seeing WHY you do WHAT you do, you can start reconditioning yourself.

_____

_____

_____

_____

How do you begin reconditioning yourself?

Create a similar list of things you could be doing differently based on what you now know about your own Ego-References, Hidden Agenda, Hidden Goal, and need to "Feel-good-about-yourself" (see graph at the beginning of this unit.) Challenge yourself.

Here is how you could go about it.

Example:

I am pretty compulsive about _finishing things I have started_ because I use it as a Vehicle to show off the Ego Reference of _not being negligent_. My Hidden Goal is to _show my parents that I am worth their appreciation and respect_.

Again, please replace the italicized text in the example above with your own scenario:

I am pretty compulsive about

_____

_____

_____

_____

_____

_____

because I use it as a Vehicle to show off the Ego Reference of

_____

_____

_____

_____

_____

because my Hidden Goal is

_____

_____

_____

_____

_____

I will try to do this differently for a week (a day, a few hours, a few minutes) and exercise my awareness of WHY I actually do that thing.

That is all you have to do. Repeat this until you're able to drop the compulsion, and the rest will take care of itself.

QUOTE FROM THE *GUIDED JOURNAL*

DAY
22

If "keeping your house clean"
is a compulsion
that you need to do
to
"Feel-good-about-yourself,"
chances are that
keeping your house clean
is a Vehicle you use
to show off
your Ego-Reference
of "being neat and organized."

Your Hidden Agenda then is to show your
caregiver/parent
that you are better than he/she thinks.

Your Hidden Goal might be to finally feel
accepted and acknowledged,
which then functions as
your
Substitute Sense of Self.

RECAP

For some, the likelihood that you are doing things because you actively choose to do them is slim. Chances are, beneath the immediate surface there lurks a Hidden Agenda and Goal behind your generosity, patience, or willingness. When "Feeling-good-about-yourself" in that particular existential way has become your life's purpose, you have to take a step back and consider why you think you need to do that in the first place.

QUIZ

Here are five questions to verify (for yourself) whether you have a good understanding of the concepts in Unit 6:

1. What is the relationship between a Hidden Agenda/Hidden Goal, and Indirect Motivation?

_____

_____

_____

_____

_____

2. What is the actual sensation of experiencing this approval-based state of "Feeling-good-about-self"?

_____

_____

_____

_____

_____

3. What phase comes next?

_____

_____

_____

_____

_____

_____

4. How can you change your old patterns of thought and behavior?

_____

_____

_____

_____

_____

_____

5. What is a good way to get started with questioning your motives?

_____

_____

_____

_____

_____

_____

REFLECTIVE QUESTIONS

Here are three reflective questions to deepen your understanding of Unit 6 as it relates to your Self:

1. Can you think of a Hidden Goal that was generated by your caregiver?

_____

_____

_____

_____

2. Do you suspect someone in your life has a Hidden Agenda? What could it be?

_____

_____

_____

_____

3. What makes you "Feel-good-about-yourself"?

_____

_____

_____

_____

LOOKING AHEAD

So much of the angst and anxiety you experience as an adult was set in motion when your parents were unable to let you develop a Healthy Sense of Self in early childhood.

In the next unit, we will speak more at length about the role parental judgment plays in the adult lives of those of without a Sense of Self. You will see how parents need not even be present for their opinions about you to linger in your mind and body. You will learn about this early and complete entanglement of parent and child that is both the cause and the result of a Lack of SoS.

NOTES

Unit 7

"Will I ever outgrow the need for approval?"

Unless you were encouraged and given opportunities from a very young age to become your own person, it's possible that you didn't develop a Natural Sense of Self. Without one, it's likely that by the time you are an adult, you find yourself constantly attempting to please others in both your personal and professional interactions—often without even being aware of it.

In an ideal situation, a Sense of Self is developed in early childhood, but there is another way for those who did not grow up with this ideal to recover their SoS later in life. Following the SoS Method can effectively free you from the internalized voice of your caregiver, a voice you have probably been mistaking for your own.

If you have a strong desire to retrain yourself, you can successfully live without the constant echo of the parental voice clouding your decision-making process. Once you silence that inner voice, you can unchain yourself from the past, stop relying on approval, and begin making your own life choices.

You can develop a strong Sense of your Self at any age—and there's no better time to start than right now.

The opinions of your childhood influencers (predominantly your caregivers/parents) still color your life in adulthood. Such coloring is normal, expected, and healthy to the extent that those opinions provide you with necessary life skills. What does *NOT* need to stay with you are the lingering residues of your parent's difficulties with their own parents and with their own Sense of Self.

Here are a few questions that might help you to get a sense of what was going on when you were growing up, if you aren't already aware of that:

- What characterized your most basic childhood experience within your family?

_____

_____

_____

_____

- If you think back to when you were growing up, is it possible your caregiver's purpose was more self-serving than was apparent to you at the time?

_____

_____

_____

_____

- On a scale of 1 – 10, 1 being ignored and 10 being adored, how would you rate your status in your family when you were growing up?

_____

_____

_____

_____

• Did your parents just quietly let you do your own thing, or were they breathing down your neck and criticizing every move you made?

_____

_____

_____

_____

• Did you feel generally respected as a person or did you feel invisible, as if you didn't exist? Did you feel you had the right to be you?

_____

_____

_____

_____

The voices you heard growing up and the vibes you received from your caregivers travel with you throughout your whole life, sometimes quietly in the background and other times like a loud, repetitive parrot. Your parents may have been loving and supportive but it is also possible that they conditioned you to be on constant alert, so you could avoid creating trouble and focus on seeking approval above all else.

This unit explores the relationship between two SoS Method concepts: Enmeshment and the Internalized Parental Voice (IPV).

When your own strong Sense of Self is absent, these two concepts can become major forces that impact and shape your adult life. They are the leading causes of excessive suffering and inner turmoil.

BENEFITS

Some benefits of gaining a Healthy Sense of Self are:

- Better social skills
- More self-confidence
- More success in business and other creative endeavors (Direct Motivation)

NEW SoS TERMS
Enmeshment / Internalized Parental Voice (IPV)

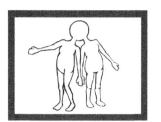

Enmeshment

An unhealthy relationship between child and primary caretaker. The child's identity and motives are merged with the adult's, which leads to extreme dependence on approval.

Children generally aim to please, but at some point, most children will exert themselves when they want space to explore their individuality. In the natural course of development, children pull away from their parents so they can become their own person.

When a child is not truly seen as an individual but is either related to as a means to an end or as a burden to the caregiver, the child is unable to develop a psychological spine of their own. What happens if unconditional love and acceptance of the child, as a unique person, isn't reflected in the virtual mirror held up by the child's caregivers? The child starts to believe that there is a reason for that and self-doubt sets in.

If the child never sees their Self as being loved and accepted for the way they are—if the child always gets a feeling of needing to be different/better, based on their caregivers' (subliminally perceived) criteria—then chances are the child takes on these non-verbal (or verbally expressed) judgments and accepts them as the truth about who they are and who they ought to be.

The child also develops ways of deflecting/preventing this judgment by making sure they live up to perceived parental expectations in an attempt to make the parent change their judgment about him or her. As the child grows up they perceive these expectations as being their own, even as a part of who they are. This is the Enmeshment situation. The child hopes that if they can meet these conditions, they might get (virtual) approval, which is *their* version of being seen as a person. This hope continues into adulthood, and can last a life time.

Maybe they would be taken into account if only they did XYZ or lived up to being XYZ. These conditions now have become what leads to some experience of a virtual, psychological spine—XYZ is now needed to fill in the **Black Hole** where a SoS should be. Living up to or doing XYZ is now an Ego-Reference (see Unit 5 for review as needed).

In an Enmeshment situation, the child's activities or behavior serve to get approval or just to be looked at in a kindly way. Trying to live up to the parent's expectations, to the point of identifying themselves with the parent becomes part of the child's "self" in the Enmeshment with their caregiver. They might eat what the parent likes or might wear what the parent likes. They tend to go places that the parent likes and never develop their own specific tastes or opinions. They make life decisions based on what the parent likes because they have never learned what it is to like something themselves. BUT THEY ARE NOT AWARE OF IT AND THINK IT IS WHO THEY ARE.*

Imagine how this pattern of behavior plays out in adult life; with partners, friends, the people they work with and for, and even their own children!

In conversations with others, later in life, this person is uncomfortable because they do not experience being *backed up* by the standards of their own opinions, tastes, and/or preferences. Perhaps they shy away from speaking up or they might instead desperately try to manifest themselves louder but end up going home with even more nagging insecurities about how they were perceived by others. They might know they have potential, but they also sense that there is an invisible cocoon around them that feels impenetrable, as if they will forever be unable to tear it open and step out as a fully developed person.

I know that feeling because I was like that. My whole life was about my parent's virtual approval and appreciation of me as-the-person-I-felt-I- was, and it created the need to "Feel-good-about-myself" on a daily basis.

*Note: Sometimes the prison created through Enmeshment and the associated lack of freedom is so stifling that a strong reaction-formation develops in which the child does exactly the opposite of whatever the parent likes, or does things to shock the parent. We call these "Reactionary Ego-References" because the child's identity is still tied up in the parent's judgment of them. The ghost voices of parental expectations are still serving as an Ego-Reference, whether the behavior represents attempted compliance, or rebellion.

A child can be so deeply Enmeshed that their entire life becomes tied to their caregiver's judgments and preferences—even long after the caregiver has passed away.

Online you can watch two videos that give a graphic representation and analysis of what the SoS Method takes as a point of departure in considering what the Self actually is (the six layers of Self) and how the process of Enmeshment between parents and children takes place. It is good to watch these video's before continuing with Unit 8, Here are the links: **Video #1 – *Building Blocks of the Self (Lego Demo)*: http://bit.ly/2hMDLk0 – Video #2 – *Interactivity of the Layers of Self (Clay Demo)*: https://youtu.be/pQVQnhObtC4**

Internalized Parental Voice (IPV)

The often-repeated verbal and non-verbal messages through which parents talk to their children becomes (almost) hardwired in the child's mind so that it is perceived as an unquestionable truth (about and) by the child.*

*Note that this is not the actual voice of your parent, this is the voice of your Belief System adopted through your caregivers' early influence.

Have you ever heard the voice of your mother or father in your head when you were about to choose an activity or behavior you knew they would not approve of? How invested in adopting (or not adopting) their values did you become by the time you were a teenager? Did you avoid certain people, careers, activities, hobbies, or lifestyles to please (or irritate) a parent? Did you pursue certain partners, friends, careers, sports, or goals for the sake of making a parent proud (or ashamed) of you?

As a child, it is not only natural to want your caregivers to express love for you and convey encouragement and acknowledgement of your existence, it is fundamentally important. What your parents think and feel about you becomes hardwired in your brain because it is repeated over and over while your brain is still forming. Eventually, it becomes part of who you are and shows up as an inner voice that is either heard or felt. That voice is *assumed* to come from your inner self: who you believe you are.

What the young child sees reflected in the mirror held up by the caregiver is *"self,"* there is no doubt about it in the child's mind. But is that reflection accurate? The mirror here can either be accurate, or—if the caregiver sees the child only in the light of his or her own agenda— it can be screamingly distorted. In that case, it can project a warped image in the child's mind of who they are, which they will try to correct for the rest of their adult life unless they question this belief.

This distorted reflection of "self" is carried out in your life through your Ego-References. That reflection is what has made you focus and work hard to get your parent to change their mind about you and give you their unconditional approval.

The IPV can be considered

the voice of your beliefs about yourself.

It is the activator of your Ego-References.

The IPV resides in your subconscious, and most of the time you cannot hear it as a physical voice in your head, but you can start to recognize it because of the symptoms it generates: fear, insomnia, heart palpitations, sweating, anxiety, anger, or rage. (And this rage is not to be underestimated. It can be a furiousness with the potential strength to kill yourself or others.) All of that is generated based on the internalized parental judgments that live within yourself. It can almost feel as if you have become your own worst enemy.

Your IPV, even though invisible (or maybe *because* it's invisible), is the toughest opponent and the hardest to eliminate.

Note: I speak about an Internalized Parental Voice but the word *voice* can be misleading. This refers to your Belief System about yourself; it is the result of a conditioning process that this course helps you undo in order to realize your own authentic thoughts and feelings.

Those inauthentic IPV thoughts and feelings mostly come down to generating fear and anger, and they can create tension in your muscles, headaches, insomnia, and depression.

These inauthentic sensations are so overwhelming that they squeeze all other feelings out of your system that would have been expressed or sensed if you had a healthy Sense of your Self and were not dependent on approval. This dependency kills any potential for experiencing your own feelings because the fear of not being able to live up to the internalized judgments ingrained in you as a child overshadows what your genuine feelings could have been.

GUIDING QUESTIONS

Who were the people you looked to for acknowledgment when you were growing up?

_____

_____

_____

Why were they unable (or unwilling) to really see you for the person you were?

_____

_____

_____

Was there ever a time when you felt acknowledged, or have you always ended up accepting approval instead?

_____

_____

_____

When you were young, in what ways or at what times was it not acceptable to be your own Self?

_____

_____

_____

_____

Name a few ways in which you *are* and a few ways in which you *are not* distinct from your parents. How have these aspects affected your experience of life?

_____

_____

_____

When were you first consciously aware that external approval was important to you? Is there some recent event that made you realize this, or have you been aware of it for a while?

_____

_____

_____

_____

How strong is the voice of your mother or father in your head when you are making certain choices, even choices as minor as what to eat for breakfast?

_____

_____

_____

_____

Can you describe the ways *your* IPV "speaks" to you?

_____

_____

_____

READING SELECTIONS FROM *HEALTHY SENSE OF SELF* – UNIT 7

Excerpts from Chapters 1, 4, and 5

"WILL I EVER OUTGROW THE NEED FOR APPROVAL?"

An Influence Throughout Life

As a child grows up and becomes more autonomous, the direct influence and impact of parents'/caregivers' behavior on the child normally diminishes. This is true for children who have developed a reasonable healthy SoS, but for those in an Enmeshment, an unhealthy degree of dependency continues through adulthood and even into old age, even though the parent's or caregiver's influence has become less visible, less obvious, and therefore less traceable. The continuation of this unhealthy relationship is often facilitated by modern ease of communication (see Chapter 7 for more on Enmeshment). Too often, for example, grown children become terribly stressed when visiting their parents, because they know they are not the sons and daughters their parents want them to be, and they feel the need of their parent's approval and validation. It's often similarly stressing when parents come to visit. A grown woman, for example, may start to clean and organize like a madwoman because her house never seems to be "good enough" for her mother. If you point this out to her, she might prefer to not look at her own behavior and to be in denial of the truth and mention futile things that justify her behavior. But when the stress level she experiences is so much higher than is justified by the actual event, it is likely that deep down inside she feels her Substitute SoS is at stake.

At any age, grown children whose parents are alive can still be needy; they still hope that by facilitating their parents' caprices they might finally get their deepest wish come true: being unconditionally loved and feeling accepted the way they are, being acknowledged as a valuable human being important in their parent's lives.

Even if an ocean lies between parents and their grown children, parents' influence can be just as present as ever within the child's inner life. The parent's standards and criteria still reverberate in his or her head and form what I call the Internalized Parental Voice (IPV).

Self-absorbed parents are unable to regard their children as anything but a pawn in the (subconsciously played) emotional games of their own lives. I call this "playing games" because their actions and world in fact have nothing to do with the reality of life in the world outside their small circle of awareness; the developmental needs of their children are part of that reality of life outside that circle.

Self-absorbed parents can never foster the development of a Natural SoS in their children because they put themselves continuously not only in the center of their own world but also in the center of other people's worlds while their child bends over backward in an attempt to get his or her need of acknowledgment as a being, as existing, met.

AN ETERNAL VICIOUS CYCLE

A parent who lacks a SoS, and who is compulsively driven to fulfill his or her perceived survival conditions makes that his or her children have to facilitate that parent's Hidden Agenda—consequently there is hardly no room for their own input, whether that be wanting to have friends over for play, engaging in activities that the parent has no interest in, or being sick or demanding attention in any way.

These patterns of behavior are likely to develop into a vicious behavioral cycle that extends over generations. The parents are not able to focus on their child and acknowledge it as a truly existing human being with all the rights that come with it. They then raise their child in such a way that, when in the situation of being a parent themselves, they will be unable to pay attention to their own children. Again they are not free from dependencies on fulfilling the Ego-References of trying to be heard and seen themselves.

THE INTERNALIZED PARENTAL VOICE (IPV)

So the good vibes of the caregiver, when no longer available, are not even directly necessary anymore. The now-grown children judge themselves by their caregiver's criteria, which they take on as their own. This approval from the virtual parent, also called the internalized parent, includes criteria that were used by the now-long-gone parent. They use these internalized parental judgments as criteria to anchor themselves in their lives through the Fgas state that then constitutes a Substitute SoS for them.

To include the presence of another voice other than your own in your Self may sound strange or even far-fetched. And truly, it took me quite a while to discover this aspect, but when looking into myself more deeply, I felt as if my parent was still present through my own voice, which really wasn't my own voice. The voice that was supposedly mine presented criteria copied from my parent, not generated by myself.

PROCEED TO THE ACTIVITY THAT FOLLOWS

ACTIVITY

When you have been brought up in Enmeshment with one (or more) of your caregivers, you choose strategies that are aimed at fulfilling your Ego-References and reaching your Hidden Goal. Once you have lived long enough to internalize these strategies, even your own body seems to remind you to keep those processes going. Can you see how, if you don't consciously object to this procedure, you end up being the victim of your own IPV?

• Do you suspect there are moments, in either your personal or professional life, when your IPV influences your decisions?

• Could these moments be improved (or avoided) by the intervention of YOUR real voice?

In the previous unit, you were invited to consult your inventory from Units 1 and 2 and to drop an activity or behavior that was tied to something important to your caregiver. Based on that activity, use the following questions to detect your IPV.

1. How did your time without that behavior feel? Was your experience positive, negative, or a mixture of both?

_____

_____

_____

_____

2. How strong was the urge to resume that behavior?

_____

_____

_____

_____

3. How did that urge manifest itself?

_____

_____

_____

_____

4. What would your parent say to you if they saw you letting go of the behavior?

_____

_____

_____

_____

5. From the way you reacted to the decision to stop the behavior, can you distill what your IPV's judgment was about it?

_____

_____

_____

_____

6. If you look at the reality of what occurs when you are *not* performing that certain behavior, what is *the factual consequence* of dropping it?

_____

_____

_____

7. On the other hand, if you consult your emotions, what FEELS to be at stake?

_____

_____

_____

_____

8. Did you find any discrepancy between reality and your emotions? What were they?

_____

_____

_____

_____

Now try to dig deeper into your IPV:
are there still things, even as an adult, you won't bring up or discuss with your parents or other authority figures because a voice in your head shuts you down as soon as you feel an urge to express yourself?

If so, what would you want to say about something that has previously felt like a dangerous or taboo topic of discussion? Imagine a situation in which you could speak freely to your caregiver without interruption. While doing this activity, monitor your emotional and physical experience.

One way to do this is to write out an imagined monologue. Another way is to look in a mirror and make eye contact with yourself, talking to yourself as if you were the one you want to safely express yourself to.

1. Speak or write as if you are really and truly being heard by the other person.

2. When done, ask yourself: How did that feel?

3. Then ask yourself: What am I willing to do in order to become strong enough to really have this dialogue?

Use this space for the imagined monologue and your responses to questions 2 and 3.

_____

_____

_____

_____

_____

_____

_____

_____

_____

_____

_____

_____

_____

_____

QUOTE FROM THE *GUIDED JOURNAL*

DAY
39

Developing your own set of values
instead of
working off the ones you have inherited
creates the difference
between
doubting and trusting
your Self.

RECAP

A child sometimes (due to unhealthy Mirroring) becomes Enmeshed with a parent and doesn't develop their own Sense of Self. The child doesn't have a Self to call "home"—a place to rest in and feel safe. Instead, indirectly, the parent is the basic reference point for the child's inner life/self. A dangerous situation develops from this: the parent (with their own unhealthy inner needs) becomes the anchor for the child's psyche, and the child must keep that anchor stable in order to feel safe.

The IPV is the voice of the belief system that is based on the parental criteria and the child's interpretation of it. This voice does not merely have a presence in the child's mind, it becomes hardwired within it, and it is perceived as an opinion of "myself."

Those living in this situation risk being in a state of constant emotional exhaustion and suffering throughout their entire lives, with the ghosts of their parent's judgment coloring everything they do. Even sadder, these children are bound to repeat the cycle of dependency with their own children if they do not take action to heal themselves and restore their Sense of Self.

QUIZ

Here are five questions to verify (for yourself) whether you have a good understanding of the concepts in Unit 7:

1. What does it mean to be Enmeshed with your parent?

_____

_____

_____

_____

_____

2. Give a few practical examples of how Enmeshment with a parent can show up in a child or adult.

_____

_____

_____

_____

_____

3. What is the root cause of Enmeshment?

_____

_____

_____

_____

_____

4. How does the internalization of a parental voice take place?

_____

_____

_____

_____

5. How does the Internalized Parental Voice typically manifest?

_____

_____

_____

_____

REFLECTIVE QUESTIONS

Here are three reflective questions to deepen your understanding of Unit 7 as it relates to your Self:

1. In what ways do you feel you may be Enmeshed with your caregiver?

_____

_____

_____

_____

2. What attempts have you made to do things differently from your parent? Have you *vowed* to never do something your parent did?

_____

_____

_____

_____

_____

3. When do you hear/feel your IPV most strongly? In what situations, if any, do think you sense your authentic feelings or preferences?

_____

_____

_____

_____

_____

LOOKING AHEAD

The next unit will connect the dots of all the insights you have gained from previous units about what happens when you grow up with a Lack of SoS. To sustain your false Sense of Self as the one and only anchor point in your life, you have to go out of your way to maintain the internal psychological mechanisms that were created in childhood. It will be revealing to see how that situation has affected your life, your real Self, and your experience of others (as well as their experience of you).

In Unit 8, all the information of the previous units comes together and will clarify for you what the SoS Theory—and Method—are all about.

NOTES

_____

_____

_____

_____

_____

_____

_____

_____

_____

_____

_____

_____

_____

_____

_____

_____

Unit 8

"Help me, mother! I sense my Self disappearing when I don't succeed in making you happy!"

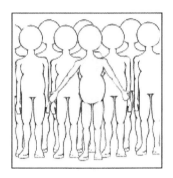

Your motive for **WHY** you do **WHAT** you do pretty much indicates how healthy or unhealthy your Sense of Self is. Here is the most important question you need to answer with utmost honesty:

Am I actually living my life?
or
Am I mainly busy fulfilling
(self-imposed) conditions?

Picture yourself sitting at a family table (you are in your forties): You're hoping to enjoy happy hour or a meal with family and friends. Who is at the table? There is the person (or people) who raised you, your siblings, nephews and nieces, and the neighbors from next door. Everybody is talking to each other and seems to be having a good time.

You joined the gathering after coming back from the doctor, where you had your ears cleaned. The procedure didn't go as expected, and you are having trouble hearing in one ear—you can't hear outside sounds, and there is a lot of noise in that ear. You try to share your story but, for whatever reason, it seems no one is paying attention. You only get this accusatory look from your caregiver that seems to convey, "You are not going to spoil this fun moment for me with your problem. Everybody is having a good time. Don't you dare!"

So you sit there, physically present but not participating; you feel excluded and ignored. You wish you could disappear... Has this ever happened to you? If so, how did it feel?

In this unit, we introduce the term *Annihilation*, which is best described as not being related to as a "real" person who matters and is taken into account. If you have no Sense of Self, you develop the habit of living up to certain conditions (Ego-References). These are based on the Early Childhood Survival Strategies you adopted in order to avoid the terror of feeling Annihilated.

Because there is so much perceived to be at stake in getting the desired outcome, these habits become compulsive behaviors. The sense of severe urgency that accompanies these habits causes reactions you may not be aware of—for example:

- You (unknowingly/subconsciously) adjust your circumstances to accommodate these habits.
- Your general mood and behavior are largely dependent on whether or not you succeed in living up to these conditions.

Building on what you have learned so far, we will now talk about a structure you may have subconsciously created—if you are a person with a Lack of Sense of Self—which functions as the placeholder for the real Self-experience.

We call this structure
a Substitute Sense of Self (SSoS)
and it determines
WHY you do **WHAT** you do.

The existence of the SSoS depends on the result you get when living up to your (often times) self-imposed conditions. As such, you and your life are ruled by the need to realize these conditions over and over again. Without the sensation of a Substitute SoS, there is no self-experience.

Can a person live and function without any Sense of Self? If that notion is hard to imagine, think of it as being similar to a person living without a backbone. The Sense of Self is the spine of the psyche. Doesn't it then seem better to have a Substitute SoS rather than no Sense of Self at all? However, the Substitute SoS needs to be *earned* over and over again. The fear of not being able to get that done results in tension, worry, anger, stress, and worse.

When a Natural Sense of Self doesn't develop, almost all life events are potential sources for earning a Substitute SoS. That explains why the stakes are perceived to be so high in many everyday events. Such stakes can produce extreme (or milder) stress and exhaustion. These, in turn, can lead to dysfunction and illness (or other deviations like violent behavior, suicide, or depression).

Gaining insight into what these aspects of your mental and emotional makeup are all about—through a course such as this one—can help you break the cycle of needing to always generate the fleeting sensation of "Feeling-good-about-self," and redirect that energy to start truly LIVING your life for other, healthier goals.

BENEFITS

Some benefits of gaining a Healthy Sense of Self are:

- Better child rearing because of greater ability to be there for their needs and joys
- Less compulsiveness
- More capable of commitment

NEW SoS TERMS
Annihilation / Fear of Annihilation / Substitute Sense of Self (SSoS)

Annihilation

A strong perception of being overlooked, not being seen and heard, not being taken into account, not having any impact in your environment, which is experienced as non-existing.

Annihilation is a big word, but imagine how you would feel if you sensed that you were being rendered invisible, reduced to a nobody— starting from the time you were born—because you were not living up to the (unreasonable?) expectations of your primary caretaker. You were only acknowledged when you did the right thing; otherwise, they couldn't deal with your presence in their already complex lives. They pushed you aside, or in many other ways made you feel that their own concerns counted more than YOU did. For you, that could have translated into feeling invisible in their eyes. That way, you were never able to simply *be you* and establish your Sense of Self.

The emphasis in such a person's life—due to the natural way infants grow and develop—is on trying to function in a way that avoids Annihilation. All of the person's capabilities are gathered to make that avoidance successful.

Fear of Annihilation
Terror of being unheard and invisible.

Annihilation is the scenario that awaits, originally when you were very young and felt ignored by your caregiver, and later in life, when you are unable to live up to your Ego-References. Annihilation is a terrifying prospect, being perceived as—and experienced as—"alive but not existing."

Trying to avoid feeling the fear of that experience later
in life can contaminate any action, activity, or behavior.

Fear of failure

The fear of failure is a good example, because it comes up when people with a Lack of SoS perform an act or a behavior that really is less geared towards the obvious result of the performance, but rather at the effect it would have on reaching their Hidden Goal. (Also see: Indirect Motivation in Unit 4 and Hidden Goal in Unit 6.)

Being able to prove that you are worth being taken into account
("Look at me, I did it!") comes down to succeeding in avoiding feeling annihilated.

Here is how it works: You do something for Indirect Motivation but you are not aware of what really drives you. You are also unaware that the Fear of Annihilation plays a role in your life. However, that fear is responsible for a greater tension in your body, for the amount of preparation you need to do something well, and for whether or not you get a good night's sleep, just to name a few of the many possible side-effects.

Substitute Sense of Self (Substitute SoS)

A psycho-emotional structure that develops as the backbone of the psyche of those children/adults whose caregivers relate to their children as an extension of themselves, and that leads to a compulsive drive for achievement-based approval.

The Substitute Sense of Self is the capstone concept of the SoS Theory. If you understand its function, then you can identify the difference between the inner workings of a person with a Healthy SoS and one with a Lack of SoS. When you lack a Sense of Self, you are bound to become dependent on a Substitute SoS.

Approval was what initially took the place of acknowledgment, and now approval
is the fundamental need and motive for much of your behavior.

The moment you (as a child or later as an adult, via the IPV) get a hint that an influential authority figure in your life approves of you, you feel temporary relief from the pain of that missing Sense of Self. The approval gives you a Fgas-state that functions (albeit only momentarily) as your Substitute Sense of Self.

As a child, you had to work very hard to get approval as a substitute for having your existence truly acknowledged.

Also as a child, you didn't know any better and felt that your caregivers were right, that you were to blame for not being worthy of acknowledgment as a unique human being with your own individual needs, thoughts, and feelings.

Consequently, you developed a strong drive to prove to them (and to yourself as well) that the reasons you were not truly acknowledged and taken into your caregiver's heart are no longer valid because you've gotten so much better at living up to all those rules and behaviors they valued above all else.

In other words: You kept working on trying to become good enough in the eyes of those who are most significant in your life, whose opinions you value, and whose love* and appreciation you crave. But the drama that plays out long after the time has passed in which you should have developed a Natural Sense of Self—even in your adult life and into old age—is you never stop trying to prove that now you are better than you felt they judged you to be back then.

Yet, you don't continuously or consciously associate your adult attempts to gain approval with the childhood memories and experiences with your caregivers—until someone, or a course of study like this, draws attention to it.

*The word "love" (to be taken into someone's heart) is generally used for a variety of emotions: familiarity—dependency—consolation—need to care for—and many others. Real love can only be experienced together with the acknowledgment of someone's being a (potentially) independent person.

How so? Later in childhood, if you have a Lack of Sense of Self, perhaps you'll seek approval by getting the best grades, being the best athlete, or the top performer (living up to those conditions may have ended up becoming your Ego-Reference). If you don't get approval for these behaviors, you will subconsciously sense that you are not good enough and, based on the fear of not really existing, you will experience the terror of Annihilation.

In order to avoid that feeling, you will try harder[1], becoming a slave to your Ego-References, always alert for ways in which you can please your caregivers (**Scanning Mode**) and/or earn a "Feel-good-about-self" as a Substitute SoS. A Substitute Sense of Self depends upon approval above all else, and you seek to get that from winning, being the best, or not being any trouble, or some other Ego-Reference.

[1] This does not imply that you could not become a topnotch performer. But it means that people with healthy motivation are more likely to succeed in what they are doing than those whose actions and goals are contaminated by the compulsion to realize their Substitute Sense of Self. When things are done for the right reasons, there are no deep fears or stresses diminishing your capabilities.

This is what it is all about: a person with a Lack of SoS acts and behaves in ways to fill the inner void left by the missing Natural SoS[2], which was unable to develop because long ago the parent was unable to truly acknowledge the child.

A Substitute Sense of Self serves as your inner spine when a Natural Sense of Self is not there to support you. Getting this substitute for the natural structure, this virtual spine, is an immediate necessity. Without this Substitute SoS, there would be this inner void which translates in you feeling on the deepest level of your being that you don't exist as a *real* person; neither for others nor for yourself (Annihilation). Seeing that connection will hopefully lead you to understand why there is so much urgency involved.

GUIDING QUESTIONS

In what ways does it feel like something/someone else is setting your standards for living?

_____

_____

_____

What are your core values for successful living?

_____

_____

_____

Can you see that it is crucial to make sure your core values are yours, as opposed to being important to someone else whom you regard as having authority?

_____

_____

_____

[2] A Natural Sense of Self is a Healthy Sense of Self that is developed at the appropriate time.

READING SELECTIONS FROM *HEALTHY SENSE OF SELF* – UNIT 8
Excerpts from Chapters 2 and 4

"HELP ME, MOTHER!
I SENSE MY SELF DISAPPEARING WHEN I DON'T SUCCEED IN MAKING
YOU HAPPY!"

Approval, Fear, the Black Hole, and Annihilation

When a parent or caregiver is unable to acknowledge their child as a "real" autonomously existing person that parent fails to provide the foundation on which their child can build a Healthy Sense of Self. The child experiences the resulting lack of Sense of Self, on a deep, primordial level of consciousness, as a painful void.

I refer to this void as a Black Hole. This void generates a gigantic power that sucks in any positive outcome of an achievement or behavior of the child that would have led to approval, which then is experienced as a Substitute Sense of Self (Substitute SoS). Any situation that goes well in the person's life and that would gain the caregiver's explicit approval is used to fill the void of this Black Hole to create, if you will, a sort of balance in the system. At the same time though failure fear is a steady companion of this success as it is success not for the sake of itself, but for the sake of gaining a Substitute SoS.

To get a full understanding of the rest of the developmental process, and the power of the unhealthy motivations that develop from this type of (Distorted) Mirroring, we need to take a close look at the child's inner experience of the Black Hole, an experience this Method calls

"Annihilation." We a/so need to take into account and study the fear developed from having experienced this void, Fear of Annihilation.

Experiencing Annihilation

In this Method, the term Annihilation is an inner, usually not consciously defined, perception of feeling as if one is alive but does not exist to others. It comes down to feeling like a person without a voice or a face as a unique individual, and comes from not being acknowledged as an independent, potentially autonomous being. The person, sensing that he or she is not being seen, heard, or taken into account, feels invisible, or is reduced to a quasi-nonexistence.

The experience of Annihilation is not so much that of existing and then not existing because of dying physically. The ultimate terror of Annihilation arises from the gut-level experience of feeling invisible even though one is physically present—present as a body but not addressed and taken in by the community. It is as if a person's authentic essence/spirit is not able or allowed to come through to manifest itself in his or her environment.

Experiencing Annihilation is not recognized as such by the person at all; it merely manifests as a rising awareness of being "off" in some way, and as a result of being discounted, it comes down to a deep feeling of being rejected, of being denied access to the world of the others.

To label this complex condition, the term Annihilation is used, rather than death or nonexistence, for two reasons.

First, there always are certain fundamental layers in the Self that do develop or exist in any kind of childhood environment, no matter how starved for acknowledgment the child is. Thus, the child can be thought of as half-alive.

Second, because whatever sense of selfhood the child subconsciously manages to achieve is always disappearing along with the approval/good vibes that (unhealthy, Substitute) SoS depends on. The physical body dies only once. Annihilation, as described here, happens over and over again.

By comparison, one could say that death is benign. The subconscious sense of not existing is experienced as terror. As we shall see, the motivation to avoid the experience of Annihilation is compelling.

Ideally the relationship between the infant and the parent(s) or primary caregiver(s) feeds the infant's sense of being acknowledged as someone existing as a separate person. This then contributes to the development of a healthy Natural SoS. This sense of being a Self is the opposite of the experience of Annihilation. If an infant's primary caregiver fails to reflect to the infant: "I see you as a being independent of me, no matter what you do or do not do," then a condition is created for a warped SoS.

What happens if a child's (person's) own needs and nature are NOT taken into account by others? The child may conclude it isn't good enough. And as it is, in that process, also being overlooked and ignored, it makes the child feel like being a ghost with a body—bodily alive but in the living hell of being invisible to everyone. An eerie suspicion of "I am not real. I have no real empowerment" may emerge in the child's or later the adult's mind. This vague uncertainty plus the strategies the child develops to try to overcome it or compensate for this feeling may stay with him or her for the whole of his or her adult life and greatly determine its quality.

I remember being present with certain groups of people and trying to mingle. I convinced myself it was normal to be overlooked and not addressed. I felt so unimportant to others, yet inside I knew I was worth a lot. I had no sense of when to come into a conversation or when to speak up in a group. I wasn't in touch with the part of your being that generates impulses and that, if you trust it, makes those decisions for you. If you have no SoS, there is no way you can rely on your intuition as you are not aligned with it.

Fearing Annihilation

Fear of the experience of Annihilation arises in young children—and then over and over again while growing up and as an adult as well, lifelong—and stems from the circumstance of not being heard and seen in their essence and not being acknowledged as independent and autonomous persons. This circumstance, which once was a reality for them, is never recognized or confirmed, though.

When a person (a parent) is with the child, feeds it, and gives it clothes, it looks like he or she cares for the child. In other words, it isn't really visible to an outsider, nor is it within the ability of a child to recognize that a parent merely tolerates the child and lets him or her come closer when the child complies behaviorally to the parent's wishes. That doesn't mean that this situation is less real, though.

I remember a situation in which, as a 12-year-old, I had an accident with my bicycle. I somehow had lost my balance and landed with my ribcage on one of the handlebars. I was in pain, but I do not remember a word of comfort from my caregiver and the trip to the doctor's office lives in my memory as a nuisance to my caregiver: "How could you do that to me?" was the non-verbal message. I don't think she really saw me.

It is hard for the grown person who has been in that situation to believe in him- or herself. There is always this uncanny sense that something is at stake: Annihilation. Now this Fear of Annihilation that lingers in one's life is the living proof of the defects in the relationship between caregiver and child. It is hard to put the finger on it later in life though, as this relationship is now only a memory.

It is the fear of not being visible as a Being, despite being bodily present, to others. The never-articulated subconscious belief is "I am unable to participate in life because nobody sees or hears me." Obviously, this leads to feelings of inadequacy and deep inferiority, and thus Annihilation becomes a constant threat and a constant reality. Fearing it, and the attempt to prevent the disappearance of anything remotely resembling a SoS, the Substitute SoS becomes a dominant motive in life.

This fear, the seed for compulsions and addictions later in life, can be so intolerably terrifying and painful that it rarely reaches conscious awareness; most people who have it experience some milder version and do not realize what they are really afraid of!

This fear is also a profound motive to gain and keep the caregiver's real or virtual approval, which allows the "Feeling-good-about-Self" (Fgas) state to soothe the state of mind.

Fear of Annihilation in a person's psyche generates a powerful force that generates compulsions and addictions in desperate attempts to avoid experiencing it. Imagine how it would be if your only experience of truly existing were while you felt good about yourself?

Thus, the Fear of Annihilation is the fountainhead for many other fears, for example, fear of not being able to access the aforementioned state of Fgas that then functions as a Substitute SoS. In short, the Fear of Annihilation is comparable to—and maybe even worse than—the fear of death.

In a person with certain early-childhood deprivations, fearing Annihilation never stops; it keeps the person in suspense (and in a "trance") for his or her whole life. It is a constant threat and a constant albeit unrecognized reality. The attempt to prevent Annihilation becomes—with the power of a force of nature—a dominant yet completely subconscious operating motive in life, and it generates an entire system of unhealthy, detrimental psycho-emotional habits, beliefs, needs, desires, compulsions, addictions, and motives. This system enslaves us until, and unless, we become aware of it.

The Substitute Sense of Self (Substitute SoS)

When a Natural Sense of Self does not develop, another structure develops in its place: a Substitute Sense of Self. It makes up for what is missing within us. Or it could very well be the other way around: Because another structure develops in the growing infant, there is no room for a natural

SoS to develop. When a healthy (i.e., Natural) SoS is lacking automatically the foundation develops of, what later turns out to become, a compulsive drive for achievement-based approval to enable the person to experience a fleeting imitation of the lacking Natural SoS.

If an ongoing sense of autonomous existence does not develop, an inner vacuum is created that leads to an intolerable terror. Subconsciously, a person then adopts various unhealthy strategies for getting positive feedback, be it physically, emotionally, verbally, or nonverbally, from his or her caregiver or parent. This feedback becomes the closest to a healthy regard that the person can obtain. These unhealthy, subconsciously self-imposed strategies include various requirements (conditions) for feeling or acting or behaving in certain ways to get recognized.

Through successfully meeting these requirements or conditions, people feel good about themselves, which is comparable with receiving a sort of validation that they "exist" as a Being. I consider this to be a substitute way of experiencing the Self, or, in other words, a Substitute SoS. The Substitute SoS is the central part of a complex collection of psycho- emotional motives, goals, feelings, needs, desires, habits, and behaviors that, as a whole, is called the Substitute SoS–Oriented System.

This system operates a great deal of the person's psyche and behavior, and has a profound influence on his or her health, relationships, work, environment, children, and spouse—in general on life itself. It causes a great deal of (unnecessary) suffering for the person who is ruled by it as well as for the people in this person's direct environment. But now that we are able to identify the condition and label it, it can, fortunately, be addressed and, with enough determination and effort, be healed.

PROCEED TO THE ACTIVITY THAT FOLLOWS

ACTIVITY

When it comes to Annihilation you experience "non-existing," which isn't pleasant. In fact, it can feel downright terrifying.

Gaining an awareness of how you react to the experience of Annihilation—when it happens at work or with family or in larger groups—would be an empowering start to being able to stop the feelings associated with Annihilation in the first place.

Learning to recognize circumstances and patterns of behavior and how you react when Annihilation is triggered is what the following exercise is about.

For this exercise, please make sure you have your inventory of WHAT you do and WHY you do it as a resource for this self-exploration. Also, be mindful of what EgoRefs you are now aware of.

Answer the following questions:

1. When was the last time you felt unseen (even though you rationally knew better)?

_____

_____

_____

_____

2. What were the circumstances?

_____

_____

_____

_____

3. What do you remember feeling in your body?

_____

_____

_____

_____

4. What messages was your conscious, thinking mind telling you?

_____

_____

_____

5. What did you do or say to the person or group that contributed to your feeling unseen and unheard?

_____

_____

_____

With that new awareness of how Annihilation has affected you, ask yourself:
6. Has this experience of Annihilation occurred at other times in your past? When?

_____

_____

_____

Reflecting on the past experiences you recall, ask yourself:
7. Are there specific circumstances or particular behavior patterns of others that trigger you?

_____

_____

_____

8. What was your deepest desire in those moments of feeling ignored?

_____

_____

_____

_____

9. How did you actually respond to the situation?

_____

_____

_____

_____

_____

10. How did any of these negative and/or frightening experiences prompt you towards making extra efforts to counter them by gaining a "Feel-good-about-self"?

_____

_____

_____

_____

11. Can you remember how far you were willing to extend yourself in order to be successful in gaining a Substitute SoS after experiencing Annihilation?

_____

_____

_____

_____

12. What feeling were you looking to realize?

_____

_____

_____

_____

_____

_____

_____

Recognizing what sets you up, what sets you off, and how you compensate for it is the skill you will need to develop.

Early detection of your inclination to react in certain ways allows for you _to stay present_ to your Self in those stressful moments and to be prepared _to keep your motivation "direct."_ It is one way to eliminate or avoid a huge amount of unnecessary stress and suffering.

QUOTE FROM THE *GUIDED JOURNAL*

Day
55

Parental mix-up

Did you ever consider
that some parents want you,
their child,
to be "just so,"
not because it is so much better,
but because it is more convenient for them?

Subconsciously, they want you to not be
present as a "real" person,
as your Self

but

as *an extension* of them!

That way, you would positively contribute
to *their* Substitute Sense of Self
and they would have more time and energy to work on
their own issues.

RECAP

If the time to develop a sense of our inner spine/home base and a healthy relationship with our Self passes us unfulfilled, we, as infants, subconsciously reach for the next-best thing. Our Substitute Sense of Self takes the place of that unfelt Self and becomes the base for our choices, beliefs, feelings, motivations—the need to Fgas has become the heart of our life/existence. It has become part of our mind-body system.

People who live their lives as a performance for others, instead of truly living it, feel the fear of failing to live up to the performance's conditions as a matter of life and death, and are bound to be continuously overwhelmed and stressed. This is a cycle that is challenging to break free of, because the need to keep the Substitute Sense of Self supported is perceived as the most important thing. So, the question is: Whose happiness matters above all else when a Substitute Sense of Self–Oriented System is active? It certainly is not the happiness and well-being of the individual with the Substitute Sense of Self.

QUIZ

Here are five questions to verify (for yourself) whether you have a good understanding of the concepts in Unit 8:

1. Specify the terms that relate to becoming dependent on a Substitute SoS for your Self-experience.

_____

_____

_____

_____

_____

2. In what way is Annihilation related to death?

_____

_____

_____

_____

3. Why does the Fear of Annihilation play such a sabotaging role in whatever you are doing?

_____

_____

_____

_____

4. Describe the relationship between (the Fear of) Annihilation and the Hidden Goal.

_____

_____

_____

_____

5. True or false: Once you experience the Substitute SoS you are fine!

_____

_____

_____

_____

_____

REFLECTIVE QUESTIONS

Here are three reflective questions to deepen your understanding of Unit 8 as it relates to your Self:

1. When do you experience the fear of Annihilation?

_____

_____

_____

_____

2. What do you do when you get stuck in trying to avoid Annihilation and your dependency on a Substitute SoS takes over?

_____

_____

_____

_____

3. When do you experience the fear of failure? How does it affect you?

_____

_____

_____

_____

_____

LOOKING AHEAD

You now have been introduced to the most important labels of the SoS Method. These labels allow you to get a sense of what the complete picture of your behavior and inner workings can look like when you lack a SoS. With that insight, you can gauge the negative spin-off of this situation in real life, which will fuel your desire to get back to who you really are and restore your Sense of Self.

In the next and last unit of this course we will examine the Substitute SoS–Oriented System and lead you through each of the concepts as they could apply to you. Getting acquainted with your own internal Substitute SoS–Oriented System is essential in breaking free from the addiction to a Substitute SoS and moving towards a healthier Restored Sense of Self.

NOTES

Unit 9
Portrait of a
Substitute SoS–oriented life

One by one we have introduced the psychological and emotional elements that are at play in the lives of people who lack a Sense of Self, to secure for themselves some sort of "self-experience," albeit through a Substitute Sense of Self (SSoS). All these elements are collected under what we call the Substitute SoS–Oriented System.

When you are not in touch with your Self because you don't even know what your Self is and how it feels, a SSoS fills in the void (what we call the Black Hole). The reality is that each and every choice, action, and behavior is geared toward getting that "Feel-good-about- self" state, because it functions as a Substitute SoS (over and over again). This particularly unhealthy situation is then augmented by the stress of feeling that you must succeed at all cost to battle the fear of Annihilation.

In this unit you will see what that looks like as a whole, and discover what the separate items are that form the Substitute-Sense-of-Self– Oriented System. Once you understand the origins of each of those elements, you will be able to effectively create lasting changes because you can now see the *futility* (despite the seeming necessity) of your (former) motivation.

You can now also forgive yourself for unintentionally allowing these conditions to play a dominant role in your life. You created these conditions a long time ago to help yourself survive, and that is what they did! So now you can say: "Thank you very much, Substitute Sense of Self. You have done your job, but it is time to go!"

A Substitute Sense of Self serves as
your inner "spine" when
a Natural Sense of Self is not there to support you.

Getting this substitute for the natural structure (the development of a Sense of Self), is crucial, as living without this virtual spine is impossible. It would be comparable to going through the motions of life, while merely vegetating as a body, without having any impact on anyone or anything around you.

So, you have to conclude that, on the one hand it is true: without a Substitute Sense of Self, your life would have been impossible. So, it did what it had to do, it helped you survive. On the other hand, you still sense on the deepest level of your being that you do not exist, either for others or for yourself (Annihilation), each time you are unable to live up to your self-imposed conditions. Seeing that connection will hopefully lead you to understand why there is so much urgency involved.

The Substitute-Sense-of-Self–Oriented System is the collection of all the various aspects and processes that are at work within you. This system is geared towards the assurance of gaining that most desired state of "Feeling-good-about-self"—which functions as your Substitute Sense of Self.

BENEFITS

Some benefits of gaining a Healthy Sense of Self are:

- More comfortable with self-expression
- Better communication skills
- Better flow in your life

NEW SoS TERMS
Substitute SoS–Oriented System / Substitute SoS–Oriented Goal

Substitute Sense of Self–Oriented System

The entire subconscious complex of needs, behaviors, motives, habits, beliefs, goals, and fears that generates achievement-based approval, which functions as an unhealthy base for being.

Below you will find an overview of the ingredients that form the Substitute SoS–Oriented System. Be advised, though, that this Unit does not give a detailed explanation of the System; the purpose is to provide you with an overview of the concepts of the SoS Method to help you better understand your own (or someone else's) behavior.

For a thorough understanding of the SSoS–Oriented System and its impact on a person's behavior (and life), You can also go to the 1st edition: *Healthy Sense of Self, How to be true to yourself and make your world a better place,* (2012) or in the 2nd edition: *The Motivation Cure, the Secret to Being Your Best Self* (2017) and in the 3rd edition: *Healthy Sense of Self, The Secret to Being Your Best Self* (2020), Chapter 8.

Most of the concepts below have been explained in the previous Units—you will find links to webpages that further explain some of the concepts.

The concepts in the SoS Method that refer to the elements of the Substitute SoS–Oriented System are:

- A lack of Sense of Self
- Self-blame
- Inauthenticity
- Annihilation and the Fear of Annihilation
- Early Childhood Survival Strategy
- Ego-References versus Quality of Life level experiences
- Hidden Agendas, Hidden Goal, Vehicles
- IPV
- "Feeling-good-about-self" Scoring
- Hindrances
- Anger, rage, depression
- Compulsiveness
- High levels of stress and anxiety
- Self-sabotage
- Extreme emotional peaks and valleys
- Specific patterns of Substitute SoS–Oriented Behavior

Other specific Substitute SoS–based fears, including but not limited to:

- fear of your own behavior;
- fear of your own emotions;
- fear of failure (stage fright);
- fear of not being able to function, fear of change;
- fear of abandonment.

The only function of the term Substitute SoS–Oriented System is to label the complexity of concepts and coping mechanisms that all play a role in the emotional makeup and behavior of a person who is dependent on approval.

Like a puppet master works a puppet's strings, the Substitute SoS– Oriented System is put in motion over and over to produce desired actions and reactions. Choices, goals, fear of failing to get to the Hidden Goal, avoidance of Annihilation, and all the aspects of a person's thoughts, feelings, and behaviors are tied together—many aspects of what they do and want are linked in some way to their ultimate goal: to get that "Feel-good-about-self" state.

There are so many ways you can realize and experience that state of "Feeling-good-about-yourself." Early in life, it can be interpreted from the embrace of your caregiver's (temporary) acceptance; it can be found in the tone of your parent's voice on the telephone, hidden in the words they use in a letter, in (potential reasons for) their absence or their presence. You continuously scan the behavior and expressions of your caregiver for approval or lack thereof. The totality of what is at work behind your obsession to Fgas is known as the Substitute SoS– Oriented System.

If we all outgrew this dependency on the approval of our parents or other authority figures we'd be better educators ourselves. We'd function better in our various roles as partners, peers, and professionals—with more self-expression and less fear of reprisal. Yet, how many of us spend most or all of our lives terrified of displeasing others?

Substitute Sense of Self–Oriented Goal

A person's subconscious, ultimate goal of convincing the parent to change his or her negative opinion about "me" into a positive one, which then gives "me" a feeling of being a "real," normal person.

Substitute Sense of Self–Oriented Goal and *Hidden Goal* refer to the same desired outcome: acceptance as a "real" person by the parent/caregiver. This new term provides a slightly different angle from *Hidden Goal*, namely as a concept within the Substitute SoS– Oriented System.

In the illustration for this term you see two people in an embrace. I love this picture because it symbolizes the Substitute Sense of Self– Oriented Goal as bringing the person with a Lack of SoS closer to their caregiver. But the pain of the reality is that it is conditional as it takes place through approval.

When you have a Lack of SoS, you are continuously seeking ways to make your parent (or other authority figure) change their mind about you so you can feel accepted. You literally crave that physical or emotional embrace—the thing that gives you your (virtual) spine/Substitute Sense of Self.

SoS terminology may be rather overwhelming to the student, especially when confronted with the subtle differences between them, so here is an overview of the various terms that could potentially be confusing:

The term *Hidden Goal* refers to how you try to get your parent's acceptance through doing the specific things they like you to do and/or behaving in the specific ways they like to see you behave. In other words, the Hidden Goal is to please them in such a way that they change their opinion about you so you no longer have to feel that it is your fault that you are not good enough to be accepted as a "real" person.

Then there are the terms *Hidden Agenda* and *Vehicles*. They describe an action or activity that is not always what it appears to be. Hidden Agendas are associated with the content of your actions, which are focused on achieving Ego-References rather than the obvious, ordinary outcome. Vehicles serve as the carriers for your Ego-References—these are actions and behaviors you perform with the intention of demonstrating the particular skills or character traits you use to get approval. Indirect Motivation lies at the root of both of these terms.

My Hidden Agenda is to prove
- that I can be on time
- that I am able to sleep through the night
- that I am not easily angered

The Vehicle I use to prove this is
- making sure others notice my timely arrival
- looking fresh and alert
- maintaining the appearance of being calm

Lastly, there are *the Ego-References*—the self-imposed requirements you need to meet so you can "Feel-good-about-self." These indicate which specific Hidden Agenda is being used in service of reaching your (Hidden) Goal.

As you have already learned, this Hidden Goal is not overt; it operates in the background on a subconscious level, both affecting and directing many of your choices and decisions.

Internalized Parental Voice: Keep in mind, there will be many instances and varieties of the parental voice that emerge in your minds during your lifetime. That is very much okay, as long as it does not feel like your sense of being allowed to exist depends on it.

In the context of family, you may always be trying to get your parent's approval, no matter your age or status in life. At work, you might be continuously seeking your peers' and/or supervisor's attention and approval. While a person with a Healthy Sense of Self might also seek attention and approval, their sense of having the right to exist does not depend on it. It's all about finding a happy balance in the effect that approval has on you. If the effect is too intense, you need to work on eradicating your need for approval by finding out WHY you do WHAT you do. Imagine it, as taking a journey through yourself—one that is ongoing.

GUIDING QUESTIONS

How does it feel when *something else* is setting your standards for living? In other words, how does it feel when you let yourself be guided by your Ego-References? Observe yourself and note the signs and symptoms.

_____

_____

_____

_____

_____

_____

_____

_____

What are your core values for successful living? Could it be that you adopted those values because they are important to someone else, someone you regard as an authority figure?

_____

_____

_____

_____

_____

Take a moment to create a mental image of what could cause you to spend all your energy on:
a. compensating for not feeling acknowledged:

_____

_____

_____

_____

_____

_____

b. avoiding the dreaded situation of feeling Annihilated:

_____

_____

_____

_____

_____

Imagine what it would be like if your life was spent living in the shadow and in the service of your caregiver.

_____

_____

_____

_____

_____

Try to imagine what it would mean to feel invisible to your family/friends.

_____

_____

_____

_____

READING SELECTIONS FROM *HEALTHY SENSE OF SELF* - UNIT 9

Excerpts from Chapters 5, 6, 7, and 8

PORTRAIT OF A SUBSTITUTE SOS–ORIENTED LIFE

Life in a Substitute Sense of Self–oriented way

Living in a Substitute SoS–oriented way is a life based on fiction because it involves, although subconsciously, a fictional Self. People live the fiction that approval is a substitute for having a right to exist and that approval is necessary to have any experience of a SoS: "I won't exist unless I get approval." They live with this in order to experience anything resembling their right to exist.

This fiction feeds and yet arises from an unhealthy compulsive cycle. Because of their subconscious perception of having their existence prolonged and not annihilated, they need the continuous influx of feeling good about themselves while never being aware of the falseness of the construct.

The term substitute in this Method connotes that a Substitute SoS is unhealthy. When a Substitute SoS is at the steering wheel of our lives, when life is guided by and anchored in a Substitute SoS, we go through life in an inauthentic way. We are not in touch with nor able to express the core of our own being, nor are we in touch with our repressed natural, authentic needs, feelings, motives, and desires.

Because the Substitute SoS has taken the place of our never-developed Natural SoS, on a subconscious level we never feel that we are fully existing, which is a cause of ongoing anger and sadness. Because of this nonexistence of an Authentic Self (Real Self), feelings are blocked or dried up, which leads to the inability to experience joy or pleasure in normally pleasurable acts.

We are guided daily by what Vehicles will best help us fulfill our Ego- References and achieve the Fgas state, we engage in activities that are not really of our own choosing. We may study music not for the joy of music, but to fulfill the desire of a caregiver, or we may wash dishes not because we enjoy a tidy kitchen, but to satisfy something else, perhaps our parents' insistence that the kitchen always be spotless.

So as you can see, in this process, although the body is not destroyed, eventually there is a near extinction of a person's spirit and psyche. The person is always conforming to something external, never free to know and express his or her real nature; the real potential Self never develops, and once the Substitute SoS–Oriented System has settled in, it becomes his or her identity.

After years of constrained, contorted behavioral compulsions from their ECSS, children start to identify with the ego-referent behavior: The behavior is part and parcel of their SoS, which is a Substitute SoS. Working to fulfill the conditions becomes not only their identity, but the only reason for living. Life for them becomes one big struggle to live up to all the (self-imposed) conditions to constantly renew this fictional identity. You can imagine how stressful this is, and what a sad situation, made even worse by the collateral damage of the side effects, sufferings, and problems.

When people do not notice this psycho-emotional pattern operating in them, they are bound to repeat it. These people are not in touch with themselves and are merely juggling as much as possible to experience the Substitute SoS. The poignant drama here is that they are skipping their lives altogether and aren't growing and maturing. In addition, these people are not the masters of their own lives; they are slaves to the force of nature that is fulfilling the Ego-References and achieving the Fgas emotional state. Life is not about them but about juggling the many. People caught in this Substitute SoS–oriented life miss out on a life that is their "own." In a way, we could even say that their worst fear is true: They don't really exist! In the long run, that can cause many diseases and addictions, big and small.

Personally, I dare say that I must have missed out on quite a number of years of active presence while being the slave of my Ego-References.

In the grip of these imperious imperatives, the only thing we see about the world and people is our own point of view, which is all about fulfillment of our Ego-References. There is no room for another person to be truly seen or heard or acknowledged as a person by us. All people are merely pawns in the game of fulfilling Ego-References, which is no game but deadly serious. And through their actions and behaviors, others sense their inauthenticity because they are perceived subliminally as being uncaring, insincere, and distant—which, indeed, they are!

The Harmful Effects of the Addiction to (or Dependency on) a Substitute Sense of Self

Unhealthy motivations, like Hidden Agendas, are fairly common, and people employing them would not necessarily be called mentally ill. Not all Hidden Agendas are equally bad; it is up to you to decide to which degree they have taken over your life. The ones that aim to compensate for past traumatic experiences tend to lead to many kinds of suffering in oneself and in others, though. The actions, which function as Vehicles for our Hidden Agendas, are, as said before, everyday little actions and activities. Still, it all may seem pretty harmless. Not so.

Here are the harmful effects that stem from Indirect Motivation and indirectly from the dependency of a Substitute SoS:

Addiction to the Substitute SoS leads to compulsive task fulfilling behavior: When behaviors have a hidden (subconscious) agenda of getting approval, they become compulsive and addictive. If succeeding in achieving the agenda feels at risk, we can erupt in rage and violence, become overwhelmed by these emotions, and not know why! Or we can become chronically depressed, as well as suffer from disease, insomnia, and many other types of human suffering, including divorce. All of these can be traced to one root cause: being motivated by the Hidden Agenda of getting approval. By cleaning up your motivation, you not only improve your quality of life; you also help make the world a better place.

Physical symptoms: I am not a doctor so I cannot go into specifics. However, it seems to me that much physical distress might be the direct result of the dependency on a Substitute SoS, including gum-disease for example and many more (see Comparison Chart and Map of Healing)

Fear-based symptoms: The various types of fear, including but not limited to anxiety, fear of failure, Fear of Annihilation, certain cases of Post-traumatic Stress Disorder, certain phobias, and general isolation.

Depression-related symptoms: Common depression. I have a hunch that there are many more symptoms that are the immediate result of the addiction to or dependency on a Substitute SoS for your self-experience.

General dysfunction: There is a lot more to say about all kinds of dysfunctions we encounter on a daily basis in our lives as well as in society as a whole, violence, suicidal thoughts or acts, divorce, greed, bullying, frequent fights in families, and many more… The purpose of this book though does not permit going into more detail about those. For now we focus on getting the SoS Method verbalized and out to the world. It is our intention as the company Healthy Sense of Self® to study all aspects of dysfunction and disease that could possibly benefit from our body of work here. We welcome any experts in those fields to join us.

Mental and/or emotional problems: Including, but not limited to: a lack of the ability to focus, heightened sensitivity to criticism, unstoppable urge to hurry up in everything you do, memory problems, learning problems (math!) for children, inability to experience feelings, problems relating to other people, and so many more…

Note that the child's Substitute SoS–Oriented Goal has now reached a new phase: The whole of the Substitute SoS–Oriented System has come into place, and it starts to rule and further form the (young) adult. In this system, the person, as he or she grows, builds on the earlier observations and strivings from childhood and, as a young adult, identifies this way of being as being him or her. Because there is no truthful way to get in touch with the Self the person is forever unable to develop any other way of existing other than through fulfilling those conditions. Such a person always needs to achieve and has no inner place to rest. This exhausting, debilitating, and stressful lifestyle is the overture to the next phase: exhaustion, burnout, or disease.

In review, we develop a Substitute SoS–Oriented System through the following experiences:

1. *We receive Mirroring from a **Distorted Mirror** (i.e., a caregiver/parent who is self-absorbed) that states, "You are not unconditionally OK," which makes us believe that we are not worth being taken into account the way we are.*

2. *From this Mirroring, we perceive that we are deficient in some way and that we are to blame for not being acknowledged as a unique human being with the right to be the way we are. We experience Annihilation (our spirit is not acknowledged). We don't develop the spine for our psyche, a healthy Sense of Self (SoS). We develop Fear of Annihilation and become totally absorbed in avoiding Annihilation.*

3. *To avoid feeling annihilated, we observe what pleases the parent and adopt complying to these aspects, turning that adaptation into our Early Childhood Survival Strategy (ECSS).*

4. *With repetition, we begin to identify with these observations and they become Ego-References.*

5. *We use Vehicles as an excuse or as a cover-up to perform the Ego-References.*

6. *Over time we strive to fulfill our Ego-References; each time with a need to complete it better than before, with one specific agenda in mind that we are not aware of— approval from the caregiver/parent or, if he or she is no longer with us, from our Virtual, Internalized Parent Voice (IPV).*

7. *When we bring our Ego-Reference to a good ending, we experience our Hidden Agenda, in other words we experience the "Feeling-good-about-self (Fgas)" state, which functions as our Substitute SoS.*

8. *Because the Fgas-state is fleeting, we have to begin the process over and over again in order to make sure we can experience it as if it were permanently available. Each time we are more determined to succeed in achieving our Ego- Reference's goal. It is this unknown goal that drives us. We are not consciously aware of it and mistakenly take it for a reason for living.*

9. *We also develop a fear of experiencing the Fear of Annihilation.*

10. *We suffer from many other Substitute SoS–oriented fears, ailments, and disorders.*

A Substitute SoS is kept in place in the person's psyche only through constant re-creation through this complex system of dependencies, conditions to be met, motivations, the Hidden Goal|Agenda, emotions, an d behaviors.

The Complex Emotional World of the Substitute Sense of Self–Oriented System

How can we start to understand the psycho-emotional makeup of a person who is governed by a Substitute SoS–Oriented System for self- experience? I refer to my own experiences here, but a detailed, "linear" description of all emotional aspects that were at play within me when I was still totally Substitute Sense of Self–oriented is hard to give.

For me, it meant that the emotions in the family where I grew up must have been quite overwhelming. In fact, as a young adult, I felt a distance between myself and most of the common things people seemed to be preoccupied with—things that would upset them or make them happy. I had made a decision not to be bothered by them and to focus on how to do things differently. Later in life though, when I became a mother, I needed to review this strategy because there was no escape from the trivialities and logistics in life at that point: I had to learn to deal with it all.

There are two predominant emotions in a person who has a Substitute SoS: the Fear of Annihilation and the Fgas state. Fear is the basic motivation for doing what it takes to get to a Fgas, and they seesaw back and forth. When one is high, the other is low. There is never a stable situation, because the Fgas state never lasts for long before it fades and requires the next "fix" of approval. When it fades, the Fear of Annihilation gets stronger. (Note that a Fgas state does not survive a good night's sleep—hence, insomnia.)

The Soup of Substitute Sense of Self–Related Goals and Emotions

The complexity of all the emotions that a Substitute Sense of Self generates in a person is best compared to soup: Everything is in it but you do not recognize the individual ingredients. So I've decided to describe my psycho-emotional makeup as if it were soup. Everybody's soup tastes differently, even though many of the ingredients might be the same. My goal in creating this description is for you to get insight into what "laws" are at work when you combine some of these psycho-emotional ingredients:

- *Normal quality-of-life events and emotions;*
- *"Holy decisions," such as "I am never going to do this or that; I am always going to be such and such; I'm absolutely going to do things in a different way compared to my parents; I am going to be different from everybody else.";*
- *The two sides of Ego-References: the normal Quality of Life motivation, for example, "not wanting anger in your house," plus the Substitute SoS–oriented motivations for not wanting to be angry (for Fear of Annihilation);*
- *Multiple simultaneously existing but incompatible Ego- References that lead to* **Inner Conflict;**
- *The "elephant in the room" of feeling good at all cost (as a family-wide Ego-Reference and Hidden Goal). I refer to the unspoken agreement (in my family of origin) that every family member makes it his or her top priority to behave in such a way that other members are provided or can preserve their Fgas as a Substitute SoS;*
- *Fear of encountering reasons to be angry, and the continuous conscious and subconscious drive to be on the lookout to avoid those. (See the issues of control in the following discussion.);*
- *Fear or one's own feelings/behavior;*
- *Fear of "screwing it up." There is perceived to be so much at stake (Quality of Life–level family peace next to the [much stronger] Substitute SoS–Oriented Goal), but we are distressed and puzzled because we are not aware of that, or of what is at stake (nor is anybody else). All we are aware of about ourselves is that we are "high-strung," that our temper is not always contained, and that in some vague, undefined way, we sense a temper display puts us back to zero, having to start from scratch. Start what, we don't know!*

We are still talking soup here:

The need to control and the constant presence of fear, stress, and the overzealous effort to do things the right way function as the binding ingredients for this soup (comparable to the function of corn starch). Throw into this pot of soup as herbs-of-the-season some random ingredients like the parental expressions such as

> *"All is wasted now" ("We had a pleasant evening, but in the end things turned sour. But all is wasted now.");*
> *"You are always the one to screw it up" (a too easily made accusation);*
> *"You blew it again";*
>
> *"I'm walking on eggshells";*

"If you are this or that way, everybody will walk out on you"; "Make sure you are not giving in to others and stay true to yourself, but I guess it is hard when you have no self"; and other similar expressions.

Put this on the fire of the Hidden Agenda (to bring the Ego-Reference to a good end), stir it really well while heating it to a boiling point, and serve it to your loved ones. Do you think they will like this soup?

PRINCIPLES AT WORK IN MAKING SOUP

Let's elaborate some more on the analogy of soup so you might get a clearer sense of the mood and mind-set of a person who is dependent on a Substitute SoS for experiencing his or her Self. There are a number of principles at work:

- *Dependency on the outcome of an Ego-Reference leads to heavy control.*
- *Ego-Reference plus Ego-Reference equals Inner Conflict.*
- *Inner Conflict leads to blaming others, rage, depression, and insomnia. A person's circumstances spiral downward. The need to repair the circumstances (make up for it by going overboard) and to control others and the circumstances even more in order not to "do it again" increases stress and fear.*
- *Self-sabotage continuously thwarts a potential good outcome to an Ego-Reference.*
- *Anger, rage, insomnia, and/or depression due to the thwarting of the Ego-Reference adds more stress.*
- *Stress plus fear equals more need to control.*
- *Stress plus need to control equals more stress; ultimately there is a point that the body and/or mind can't handle it anymore and falls ill from exhaustion, fear, and depression.*

PROCEED TO THE ACTIVITY THAT FOLLOWS

ACTIVITY

Disclaimer: You might experience some resistance in this unit, but push through it and stay the course. It's about to get even better as you move toward knowing what to do to Restore your Sense of Self.

Working out the following tasks can give you extensive insight into your own Substitute SoS–Oriented System, if you have one:

1. Which concepts that form the Substitute SoS–Oriented System can you recognize in your behavior?

_____

_____

_____

_____

2. Describe how you were mirrored to by your parent or caregiver. Did they really *see* you? Go back in time and watch the "movie" of your own early childhood. What was at play? What was your place in that situation/drama?

_____

_____

_____

_____

Self-blame: What is your level of self-blame? Can you come up with an overview of what you were blamed for—even while you were trying to please your caregiver? How much of that blame has stayed with you and how much do you see as really being your fault? Question those conclusions by thinking things through for your Self now— independently—with your own mind!

_____

_____

_____

_____

Inauthenticity: How do you relate to the concept of inauthenticity? Do you feel like you live an authentic life? Are you true to your Self? If so, in what? If not, in what?

_____

_____

_____

_____

Annihilation and the Fear of Annihilation: What does this mean for you? Has Annihilation played a significant role in your life? What situations generate the Fear of Annihilation in you?

_____

_____

_____

_____

Early Childhood Survival Strategy: List the known strategies you used when you were young to get positive vibes and approval from your parents. Highlight those that are still active in your life.

_____

_____

_____

_____

Ego-References: List any Ego-References that you are aware you have now or have had in the past. Highlight those that are still active. If you have any past Ego-References that are no longer active, think about what occurred to deactivate them.

_____

_____

_____

_____

_____

Hidden Agendas: Can you come up with a Hidden Agenda for each of the Ego-References you have listed?

_____

_____

_____

_____

Vehicles: Can you think of any Vehicles you use for those Ego-References?

_____

_____

_____

_____

Hidden Goal: What is your Hidden Goal?

_____

_____

_____

_____

_____

Internalized Parental Voice: The IPV is the voice of your belief system. Refer back to the activity in Unit 7, can you refresh yourself on what ways your IPV manifests itself? In other words, what signs or symptoms does your body show when some internalized criteria are being ignored, overlooked, or not performed to perfection?

_____

_____

_____

_____

To ***"Feel-good-about-self"***: What is YOUR version of "Feeling-good-about-yourself"? How would you describe that state with your own words? When was the last time you can remember reaching the Fgas state?

_____

_____

_____

_____

Scoring: Can you think of a few ways you would try **To Score** for your caregiver's approval?

_____

_____

_____

_____

Anger, rage, and depression: Determine if anger, rage, and depression play a predominant role in your life/behavior. Describe the circumstances that cause them to arise:

"I am often angry when…" _____

_____

_____

_____

_____

"I am enraged when…" _____

_____

_____

_____

_____

"I feel depressed when…" _____

_____

_____

_____

_____

_____

Compulsiveness: Do you feel the need to do certain things at all cost and cannot quite clearly understand why? List some of your compulsive behaviors. Describe a situation that instigates compulsiveness in you.

_____

_____

_____

_____

_____

High stress and/or anxiety: When do you experience high stress or anxiety? List the things/people/situations that cause you to feel this way. Do any of the causes justify the intensity of your stress or anxiety?

_____

_____

_____

_____

_____

Other Substitute SoS–oriented fears: Please consider each of these fears, one by one, and whether any of them apply to your own inner makeup:

Fear of your own behavior: Are you worried that whatever you do or whatever decisions you make will lead to the opposite of what you are trying to achieve? Do you worry that you are not nice enough? Haven't been kind enough, haven't treated a person with enough respect, haven't paid enough attention to *their* story?

_____

_____

_____

_____

Fear of your own emotions: Many parents make it clear, verbally or non-verbally, that they prefer their children not to express (or even have) negative emotions. Because of your dependency on their approval, it could very well be that you force yourself to accommodate these wishes. In this situation, expressing your own negative emotions (anger, sadness, etc.) thwarts your ability to get that sense of safety (Fgas) that you so desperately need.

On top of that, suppressing these emotions creates undue complexity within your psyche, which frequently leads to sudden explosions of rage. These bouts of anger or temper tantrums are exactly what you were trying to avoid in the first place.

Do you dread not having the appropriate or most convenient emotions at times? In other words, do you fear not being able to deal with certain situations?

_____

_____

_____

_____

Fear of failure (stage fright): Are you ever extremely anxious that things will not work out or that you won't do well, despite being fully prepared? Do you freeze up or does your mind go blank in certain situations? What symptoms do you experience when this fear arises? Are they emotional, physiological, or both?

_____

_____

_____

_____

_____

Fear of not being able to function: The perceived dependency on a Substitute SoS leads to extreme worry that something will prevent you from gaining it. Without a Substitute SoS, you experience the most dreaded feeling of Annihilation, which makes it difficult, if not impossible, to function at the level necessary for you to Fgas (which serves as your Substitute SoS). To avoid this negative cycle, you focus on perfecting your performance of actions and activities towards gaining a Substitute SoS. Is this applicable to your life/behavior? At what times do you feel you are putting on a performance rather than acting as your true Self?

_____

_____

_____

_____

_____

_____

_____

Fear of change: Are your current lifestyle and surroundings (housing, relationships, job, etc.) organized in such a way that you will be able to work your way up to Fgas? If anything changed in your situation, would it prevent you from reaching the Fgas state? Does the thought of change provoke anxiety? Why do you think that is and how would it manifest for you?

_____

_____

_____

_____

_____

Fear of abandonment: Consider your relationships with those closest to you (your spouse, parents, friends, etc.) Are you ever afraid of being abandoned if you do or say certain things? Does anyone actually give you reason to believe they will abandon you or is it possible that it exists only in your own mind? Are there any triggers that remind you of your childhood situation?

_____

_____

_____

_____

_____

_____

_____

Emotional roller coaster: Describe the overall levels of your emotional life on a daily, weekly, monthly basis. Do you ever feel that your emotions fluctuate more than is usual or that you lose control of them? Are there any specific situations that make you feel like you're on an emotional roller coaster?

_____

_____

_____

_____

_____

Specific patterns of behavior: How might you draw a graph of your ups and downs? Do you notice any specific patterns of behavior? If so, consider what created this pattern within you.

_____

_____

_____

_____

_____

_____

_____

_____

_____

QUOTE FROM THE *GUIDED JOURNAL*

DAY
73

Tricky

So often
we tend to use our healing
to persevere with even more tenacity in making
the mistakes that cause our pain in the first place.

We think
we know what is good for us
better
than Nature.

Are you ready to give up
what hasn't worked for you so far
or
do you intend to use your healing
to make
what you were trying to achieve
work after all?

RECAP

The soup of the Substitute Sense of Self–Oriented System has been served to you. That is *a* soup, with a distinct number of ingredients. I could imagine, as the author of the SoS Method, that the list of ingredients in other people's soup would be slightly different, depending on your cultural background, the materials available to you, or your talent for cooking. It is absolutely useful to at least be acquainted with your own recipe and with that of your significant other, so you can learn to see where behavior comes from. It'll make discussions easier and more fruitful.

The best thing to do is, of course, to get rid of all these specific aspects that only serve to gain the Substitute Sense of Self–Oriented Goal. The one and only thing you have to do is eliminate your Hidden Goal. That occurs when you understand that you no longer need of a SSoS because *you ARE already*, and integrate that new understanding into your life. Now you are aware that you need to focus on *sensing your Self*, and that you no longer need to work your way up to a "Feel-good- about-self" state on a daily basis.

That means that you can live your life for you, without external approval, which has always been your Hidden Goal. Eliminating the need for this approval makes the whole of the Substitute SoS– Oriented System obsolete.

When you can integrate the awareness of this chain of cause and effect in your life, it is highly likely that you will experience a great number of positive changes. There is no quick fix, though; patience and dedication are needed to grow this awareness.

To enable your success in the matter, we are developing a second course that is focused on the process of how to recover from a Lack of Sense of Self.

QUIZ

Here are three questions to verify (for yourself) whether you have a good understanding of the concepts in Unit 9:

1. Where does the Distorted Mirror fit in the Substitute Sense of Self– Oriented System?

_____

_____

_____

_____

_____

_____

_____

2. What are some parts of a Substitute Sense of Self–Oriented System?

_____

_____

_____

_____

_____

_____

_____

3. In the Sense of Self Method, what is a person's most important motivation for realizing a Substitute Sense of Self–Oriented Goal (Hidden Goal)?

_____

_____

_____

_____

_____

_____

_____

_____

_____

_____

_____

_____

_____

_____

REFLECTIVE QUESTIONS

Here are four reflective questions to deepen your understanding of Unit 9 as it relates to your Self:

1. Did you experience any resistance when working through the activity? How did you move past it?

_____

_____

_____

_____

_____

_____

2. Can you sense when you are stuck in the Substitute SoS–Oriented System?

_____

_____

_____

_____

_____

_____

3. Which Substitute SoS–oriented fears are most difficult for you to deal with? Why?

_____

_____

_____

_____

_____

_____

_____

4. Remind yourself of the goal you had in mind when you began this course. How are you doing with that? How much progress have you made?

_____

_____

_____

_____

_____

_____

_____

FINAL COMMENT

In this workbook for the Sense-of-Self Method Course, you have been exposed to a great number of new concepts. As you learned more about them you compared them with what happens within your own Self. Chances are that you are already integrating many of the specifics of the SoS Method without actively taking the initiative to do so. Actively taking the initiative will accelerate and amplify your healing process!

This course—and with that your first step—now has come to an end. However, it would be very wise to not set it aside. Rather, to best benefit your Self, you should continue actively using the material. Restoring your SoS is a lifelong process. The more active you are, the more you achieve.

Understanding what drives your behavior allows you to
make lasting changes that can lead to living a more
conscious, empowered life. You will thrive with the firm
conviction that

you never have to do anything to deserve your life

because

you already *are*

and

**you always have the right to exist as
YOU!**

NOTES

The Twelve SoS Reconditioning Statements

I am ready to be part
of a healthy community

XII

I am ready to share
my life with others

XI

My life and my body
are mine

I

Relapse is always
lurking

X

I experience
myself directly

II

My work is aimed
at the obvious,
direct outcome

IX

I am present to
the Here and Now

III

I have conversations
to transfer information
or to connect with others

VIII

I think
for myself

IV

I see other people
for who they are

VII

V

I am consciously aware
of my senses

VI

I have access
to my own feelings,
preferences and opinions

THE TWELVE
SOS RECONDITIONING STATEMENTS

The Twelve Reconditioning Statements are the core of the SoS Method. They may seem like simple and obvious truths but chances are that in practicality you are out of alignment with them. These statements are prompts to help you develop a visceral understanding of your Sense of Self. Each prompt is an exercise in thinking, feeling and bodily awareness. Repetition and practice of these exercises will turn them into automatic thoughts and feelings, replacing your earlier unhealthy statements (that weren't even true) but in which you had placed your faith without having chosen them consciously.

I   My life and my body are mine.

II I experience myself directly.

III I am present to the Here and Now.

IV I think for myself.

V   I am consciously aware of my senses.

VI I have access to my own feelings, preferences, and opinions.

VII   I see other people for who they are.

VIII   I have conversations to transfer information or to connect with others.

IX My work is aimed at the obvious, direct outcome.

X   Relapse is always lurking.

XI I am ready to share my life with others.

XII   I am ready to be part of a healthy community.

For a deeper exploration of each statement and a detailed support for practice you can also go to the 1st edition: *Healthy Sense of Self, How to be true to yourself and make your world a better place*, (2012) or in the 2nd edition: *The Motivation Cure, the Secret to Being Your Best Self* (2017) and in the 3rd edition: *Healthy Sense of Self, The Secret to Being Your Best Self* (2020), Chapter 14.

Glossary

Annihilation

A strong perception of being overlooked, not being seen and heard, not being taken into account, and not having any impact in one's environment, which is experienced as non-existing.

Black Hole

Metaphor for an intolerably terrifying emptiness or invisibility as experienced by a person with a Lack of Sense of Self who doesn't feel like (they are considered) a "real" person.

Like a force of nature, the Black Hole sucks in behavior and achievements that can potentially lead to *approval*. It fills itself with anything that serves as a Substitute Sense of Self, which immediately leads to anxiety about losing the Substitute Sense of Self.

Direct Motivation

Motivation that is ordinary, simple, and based in the present.

Direct Relationship with Self

A way of relating to your own being that includes body awareness, which means that you sense your Self without having to refer to achievements or other people's opinions about you.

Distorted Mirror

The process by which the primary caregiver is unable to effectively acknowledge their child(ren) as a separate being(s), as the caregiver is too wrapped up in their own problems and emotional neediness.

The child inevitably and naturally concludes that he or she *IS* the way he or she sees him- or herself reflected by the caregiver, which is, in the light of the child's mind, an understandable but incorrect conclusion that can have far-reaching negative implications.

Early Childhood Survival Strategy (ECSS)

Conclusion to take refuge in gaining approval, drawn instinctively by infants/toddlers/children when their needs of feeling acknowledged as separate (unique) individuals by their caretakers are not met. This process becomes the foundation for Indirect Motivation, which leads to an unhealthy way of experiencing the Self.

Ego-References

Subconsciously accepted requirements to feel and behave in certain ways and achieve certain results in order to feel approved of, as a substitute for a healthy way of experiencing the Self.

Enmeshment

An unhealthy relationship between child and primary caretaker. The child's identity remains under- or undeveloped and his or her motives stay geared toward getting the adult's approval, which leads to extreme dependence on approval.

Fear of Annihilation

Terror of being unheard by and invisible to others.

"Feel-good-about-self" (Fgas)

An emotional state (or thought) of relative well-being and safety based on the absence of feeling compelled to produce certain results at all costs, gained from succeeding to comply to the wishes of the caregiver, which leads to approval. It serves as a temporary and unhealthy substitute for a sincere sense of being alive (as a "real" person).

Focus Mode

Relaxed movements of the eyes, with the ability to stay fixed in the same place for extended periods, and which indicates a grounded mood or a person with a Healthy Sense of Self.

Healthy Sense of Self

The ability to experience and be present to your own person and to your own life and recognize both as uniquely owned by YOU. That includes the right to live and be as your Self and experience your innermost core as your ultimate home from where you live your life.

Hidden Agenda

A subconscious purpose that drives your actions or behavior, which is not the obvious, ordinary, expected purpose but the demonstration of the ability to perform an Ego-Reference to perfection, as a path to feel safe and on your way to achieving your Hidden Goal.

Hidden Goal

Your subconscious ultimate objective of getting the approval of your caregiver as an unhealthy substitute for feeling valued and related to (acknowledged) as a "real" person.

Hindrance

Any obstacle on your path to gaining a Substitute Sense of Self that frequently leads to anger or rage, which can be a gateway to violence or its counterpart, depression.

Indirect Motivation

The motive for doing or avoiding something is not what it appears to be; instead, the motive is to accomplish your Hidden Agenda and ultimately your Hidden Goal, which leads to a temporary emotional state that is the substitute for a lasting sense of being a "real" person.

Indirect Relationship with Self

Sensing yourself as a "self" through achievements or the responses of others, which gives you a temporary good feeling instead of a healthy abiding sense of being who you are.

Inner Conflict

Two or more competing and incompatible inner mandates to work toward experiencing a Substitute Sense of Self. This leads to high anxiety because the competition causes a no-win outcome.

Internalized Parental Voice (IPV)

The often-repeated verbal and nonverbal messages that parents, knowingly or unknowingly, transmit to their children becomes (almost?) hardwired in the child's mind so that it is perceived as an unquestionable truth (about and) by the child.

Lack of Sense of Self

Characteristic of a person who never developed a natural, ongoing inner knowing that he or she is truly alive as a "real," independent human being.

Magic Formula

A way of remembering the gist of the SoS Method: Move away from the addiction to "Feeling-good-about-yourself." First cross out the judgmental word "about" – don't be *about* your self – be yourself! Next cross out the word "good" – no need to point that out: *good* is your default state. What is left is: Feel your Self = sense your Self = have a Healthy Sense of Self!

Mirroring

The mutual and subconscious verbal and nonverbal processes by which the primary caretaker conveys basic feedback to the child about whether the caretaker relates to the child as independently existing individual or as a means to fulfill the caretaker's emotional needs – this message functions as a mirror for the child and is accepted as the truth of who the child is.
The adequacy/inadequacy of the way this mirror functions is a decisive factor in the child's development (or lack thereof) of a Sense of Self of their own.

Motivation

In general, motivation is what creates an incentive or urge to do or avoid something. Motivation is the drive that determines behavior.

Motivation Check

A crucial (verbal) tool, which serves to a) detect your (Indirect) Motivation and b) record your Ego-References and Hidden Agendas, and to get insight what your Hidden Goal is.

Natural Sense of Self

The subconscious sense – developed normally in childhood – of being alive as a "real," definite person, with the unconditional right to exist as who you are, regardless of what others think, feel, or say about you.

Quality-of-Life Level

A healthy level of experiencing life's events and responding to them with emotional reactions that are in sync with the degree of intensity of the actual effect of these events or behavior of others on your life.

It is indicative of a Healthy Sense of Self and distinguished from a (usually unaware) dependency on a Substitute Sense of Self where for the same type of events emotions are experienced that strike down to the level of your sense of existence-as-a-self.

Real Self (Authentic Self)

The totality of one's body, mind, and emotions and what comes with being a person is experienced in the healthiest, most integrated way as an independent and autonomous being; actions and awareness are based on living experience, not contaminated by pathological motives.* See also Natural Sense of Self.

*Not so much meant in a spiritual sense but more as a reference to the whole person you really are.

Restored Sense of Self

The end result of working with the SoS Method, which is being healed from the dependency on a Substitute Sense of Self and which consists of a steady awareness of being one's very own person who is free to live life based on one's own essence, preferences, abilities, and limitations.

There is an inner knowing of being separate from any parent or caregiver and free from any dependency on achievements or approval. There is an abiding sense of being (unconditionally) alive and "real."

Scanning Mode

A person's eyes moving around restlessly, searching for opportunities "To Score," which would fill the need for approval and "Feeling-good-about-themselves." Scanning mode use of the eyes indicates activity aimed at achieving an unhealthy way to experience one's self.

Sense of Self (SoS)

A conscious and/or subconscious awareness of existing independently as a unique and potentially autonomous human being.

Substitute Sense of Self

A psycho-emotional structure that develops as the artificial backbone of the psyche of those children/adults whose caregivers relate to their children as an extension of themselves, and that leads them to develop a compulsive drive for achievement-based approval.

To Score

Being successful in using a Vehicle to improve on an Ego-Reference; a success that feels like gaining points toward the Hidden Goal,* which results in a "Feel-good-about-self" as a placeholder for the real-self experience.

*The Hidden Goal does not necessarily always have to be parental approval. It also can be the undoing of early childhood traumatic experiences, such as being bullied, not being accepted by peers, etc.

Vehicle

An action, activity or behavior used to display the performance of specific skills or character traits rather than the obvious, ordinary goal. The performance is ultimately aimed at getting approval (Fgas).

Quiz Questions and Answers

INTRODUCTION

1. What is a Sense of Self?

A Sense of Self is an unshakable inner knowing that you are your own person with your own past, present, and future, with your own principles, opinions, preferences, and tastes, and the ability to use that awareness as a solid base from which to live. If things go according to plan, you gain this awareness in childhood. Your parents or caregivers would encourage self-discovery, and acknowledge your individuality. They would also be able to provide the correct example through living by their own values and standards, rather than those they inherited from *their* parents. A child learns what their parents live, and growing up in a healthy environment promotes the development of a healthy SoS.

But sometimes things go awry. When you grow up in a household where being accepted depends on your ability to please your parent, then developing a sense of your true Self is hindered. That means that later in life you have to work extra hard to recondition your subconscious mind so you can gain this same awareness that comes to others so easily. It's a bummer, all right, but it can be done. And believe me, anything is better than staying addicted to approval for the rest of your life.

2. What are the most important aspects of the Learning Agreement you have made with your Self?

To help you remember the reason you started this course in the first place. Sometimes your intentions are good but it can be so easy to let something distract you from your goals.

Especially with a subject like this one, which can be quite prickly indeed. When you feel resistance or when dredging up the past becomes painful, you might be inclined to use anything as an excuse to quit. To prevent this, the learning agreement helps you to stay true to your intentions.

We suggest you give yourself a reward for continuing whenever you feel you want to quit. Never give up on your Self. There is so much at stake: the freedom to be you!

Unit 1

1. *How can you solve many of your issues?*
You can solve almost all of your problems by knowing WHY you do WHAT you do.

The reasons you have for doing things or avoiding them have a lot to do with your ultimate goal in life.

Your ultimate goal is determined by the level of your Sense of Self: If you have a Healthy Sense of Self, you're doing the things for their own sake. If you have a Lack of Sense of Self, your reasons are rooted in your past and are stored in your subconscious mind. Those reasons though, may turn out to no longer be beneficial.

Without you being aware of it, you may still be driven to gain approval from that most important person in your life, usually the one who raised you. Unfortunately, if you ended up with a LoSoS, this person failed to acknowledge and value you as your own unique and potentially autonomous human being. That was—and is—a crucial pain point in your life and you are still trying to make them change their mind about you.

2. *Why is it important to be completely honest with yourself?*
It is extremely important that you be completely honest with yourself because this determines whether or not you will achieve the desired result: solving the problems that made you decide to take this course.

Most people have a strong urge to "Feel-good-about-themselves" at the expense of everything else. This makes it tempting to bypass hard-to-accept truths about yourself and about your loved ones.

However, to benefit from your work with the Sense of Self Method, you have to make sincere efforts to discover these truths and not shy away from any confrontation.

3. *WHY is it important to know the reason for WHY you do WHAT you do?*
Knowing WHY you do WHAT you do sheds light on the nature of your motivation, which gives you insight into what you are all about.

Your motivation can be healthy or unhealthy. Unhealthy motivation is based on a Lack of Sense of Self and can be the source of serious problems. Healthy motivation is an indicator that you are a person with a Healthy Sense of Self, which makes you more prone to being happy and successful.

The goal of the Sense-of-Self Course is to help you cure your motivation, shifting it from unhealthy to healthy. By curing your motivation, you are healing your Sense of Self so you become the master of your Self. This way, you are setting yourself up for a happy and successful life.

Unit 2

1. *How can a Sense of Self be Natural?*

You can claim to have a Natural Sense of Self if you effectively grew up to be your own person. That means your parents have lead by example as well as given you the necessary support to develop your own Sense of Self.

If you grow up like this, your Sense of Self grows with you, becoming an intrinsic part of who you are. When you have a Natural SoS, asking yourself whether or not you have a SoS becomes obsolete. Your SoS is so interwoven into the fabric of your being, so you will have a hard time answering that question because you don't know what if feels like to lack a SoS.

2. *What is a Lack of Sense of Self and what effect does it have on a person's life?*

A Lack of Sense of Self is the absence of a permanent inner knowing that you are your own person, that you are a real and independent human being. That notion does not exist in you because, in your childhood, its development was set aside to give priority to other things.

If you are a person with a Lack of Sense of Self, the criteria you use to judge things—and especially yourself—are enmeshed with the values and desires of your parents/caregivers. You don't know what *you* want and you're looking to others for guidance, ideas, and standards to live by.

However, continuously living up to other people's criteria because you are in need of their approval induces fear, frustration, and stress. In the long run, this has a self-destructive effect on you.

3. *Is pleasing your parent/caregiver always a good thing?*

It is always good to be nice to people if it is based on a healthy intention. But if you're acting from a Lack of Sense of Self, there is a high risk that you're pleasing your parents to get their approval so that you can "Feel-good-about-yourself." This is an unhealthy condition that has to be healed as soon as possible.

The same reasoning applies to "giving" to others. You can only truly give something to people, if you don't need anything in return from the other person. The moment you give because you are in need to receive appreciation or approval, your gift doesn't come from the heart and simply doesn't hit home.

Unit 3

1. *Describe in a few words what an Early Childhood Survival Strategy is.*

The ECSS is a collection of conclusions drawn when you are a child.

Its purpose is to help you meet your need for parental attention when you don't feel acknowledged as your own unique, potentially autonomous little person.

In other words, this strategy is born if your parents are too self- absorbed to truly see you as an individual human being with a life of your own, and instead relate to you as a pawn in the game of their own lives.

In this early stage of your life, approval is often mistaken for acknowledgment. The moment this parental acknowledgement of you as your own person doesn't take place, your goal as a child becomes to gain their approval instead. This process becomes the basis for an unhealthy way of experiencing your Self.

2. *What is Mirroring and why does it matter?*

Mirroring is the subtle, mutually subconscious process by which the caregiver conveys to his or her child a sense of either being a means to fulfilling the caretaker's emotional needs or being a "real" and unique person—a sense that the infant accepts as the truth of who he or she is. If you could talk to your parent/caregiver from an early age, the very first questions you would probably want to ask them are: "Do you see me? Do you accept me for who I am?"

3. *How are Mirroring and Early Childhood Survival Strategy linked to one another?*

The ECSS is created when, as a child, your *need to feel acknowledged as your own person* is not met due to your caregiver's inadequate Mirroring.

As a child, you feel forced to transform yourself in such a way that you stand a better chance to live up to the criteria you know you need to meet to get your parent's approval.

By doing so, you still hope they will acknowledge your existence as your own person, but unfortunately, since it is not your fault that you didn't get that acknowledgment, all you get is their approval.

Unit 4

1. *What is Motivation?*

Generally speaking, Motivation is a stimulus to do or avoid something. Motivation drives behavior based on a desire you have.

It may be a desire to realize a wish you have, to satisfy your curiosity, or to alleviate pain.

2. *Describe the difference between Direct and Indirect Motivation.*

Direct Motivation is straightforward and based in the present. There is a well-defined goal and the focus is fully on reaching that goal. There is no subconscious Hidden Agenda to meet a need from the past or ease a pain from the past.

By contrast, Indirect Motivation is complex and not what it seems to be. Indirect Motivation is not about WHAT you're doing, but rather about WHY you're doing it. The real motive for doing or avoiding something stems from the past and has nothing to do with the apparent goal.

In the case of Indirect Motivation, your behavior is driven by the compulsion to get approval. Getting approval makes you "Feel- good-about-self." This state of Fgas functions as your artificial Sense of Self when a Healthy Sense of Self is missing.

Reaching this state is therefore experienced as a matter of life and death. And because the stakes are perceived to be so high your stress levels are extreme and you can't afford to aim at anything less than perfection.

However, you are not aware of this unhealthy aspect of your motivation.

3. How does Indirect Motivation relate to your Sense of Self?
The level of your Sense of Self determines the type of motivation from which you act.

When you have a Healthy Sense of Self, you're doing the things for their own sake, which means that you act from a healthy Direct Motivation.

If you have a Lack of Sense of Self, your motivation is Indirect and unhealthy. You're doing things to get approval from your parents, caregivers, or other authority figures.

If you want to *cure your motivation*, you must start by restoring your Sense of Self!

Unit 5

1. How was the SoS term "Ego-Reference" born?
"Ego" is another word for "I," but it does not refer to your real SELF. In the SoS Method the word *ego* is used to indicate a so called artificial Sense of Self—the fake SoS that is there to fill the inner emptiness that exists in a person with a LoSoS.

An Ego-Reference refers to the way this false SoS is generated: by performing a quality or characteristic to a specific, personalized high standard.

To perform an Ego-Reference, you use a specific activity or behavior as a carrier or Vehicle. Its purpose is to gain approval by showing off that you are good enough after all. That approval leads you to Fgas, which functions as this artificial Substitute SoS. Performing Ego-References is an act of Indirect Motivation.

2. Are Vehicles real cars? What are they used for?

No, in the Sense of Self Method, a Vehicle is an activity, behavior, or event that is used to demonstrate an Ego-Reference.

For example:
Sending thank you notes can be the Vehicle for the Ego-Reference of "being attentive" (in contrast to what you think causes your parents to disapprove of you). Or tidying up your house can be the Vehicle for the Ego-Reference of "showing that you are not a messy person."

Vehicles are carriers for Ego-References. They provide opportunities to demonstrate that you DO know how to do something or that you CAN perform in those specific ways that please your parent.

If you have a Lack of Sense of Self, you are always looking for Vehicles to show your parents or other authority figures that you are better than they thought (or than you think they thought).

3. What important concept of the Sense of Self Method are Ego- References and Vehicles closely related to?

Ego-References and Vehicles are closely related to Indirect Motivation and Early Childhood Survival Strategy.

Performing Ego-References is an act of Indirect Motivation. They are the results of a process of trial and error that takes place in early childhood and that has as the purpose of finding ways to get your parent/caregiver's approval. What was discovered to be successful turned into a strategy.

Vehicles are the opportunities to carry out and demonstrate those strategies so that you receive the desired approval.

Sometimes you create Vehicles and sometimes you use already existing Vehicles.

For example: You can wash your father's car when he asks you to, thereby earning the desired approval. The car needed to be washed anyway.

But you can also approach your father and create a Vehicle by offering to wash his car. You may claim that you're doing this because the car is dusty, but in reality you wanted to create an opportunity to get your father's approval. Maybe your father was angry at you and that made you feel uncomfortable, even painfully uncomfortable. This way you are trying to change his mind about you and "Feel-good-about-yourself."

Unit 6

1. *What is the relationship between a Hidden Agenda/Hidden Goal and Indirect Motivation?*

Indirect Motivation means that you're doing things for something other than the obvious reasons, with the actual purpose being th realization of your Hidden Agenda: proving that you are good enough after all.

The use of Indirect Motivation serves as a tool to help you reach your ultimate Hidden Goal, through tackling an Ego-Reference and fulfilling its Hidden Agenda.

That ultimate Hidden Goal is initially to try to get your parent to confirm your existence as a potentially independent but nevertheless valuable son or daughter. But since your parent is unable to play an adequate part in that process, you end up having to settle for approval.

2. *What is the actual sensation of experiencing this approval-based state of "Feeling-good-about-self"?*

In the SoS Method, the "Feel-good-about-self" state does not indicate a state in which you feel happy, although that can be the case at times, but this term refers to the experience of a moment of temporary relief from the compulsion to perform Ego-References to perfection and live up to the high standards of your parent/caregiver. This includes a temporary relief from the urge to make that person "Feel-good-about-you" so you can get his/her approval.

3. *What phase comes next?*

Due to the absence of a Healthy Sense of Self, there is an inner emptiness that needs to be filled. A "Feel-good-about-self" state fills that hole and functions as an artificial Sense of Self. That is why the need to reach that state is experienced as a matter of life and death and becomes compulsory.

So, after a short period of relief, the urge returns to prove that "you can do it," or that you are capable of performing in that specific way that pleases your parent.

"Feeling-good-about-self" is a state that can be achieved through anything: accomplishing something that potentially qualifies for approval, satisfying an Ego-Reference, or, for example, a positive encounter with your parent that gives you a brief moment of feeling wrapped in his or her attention.

4. *How can you change your old patterns of thought and behavior?*

First you need to be able to identify those old patterns of thought and behavior. Once you discover that they are all about getting the approval that makes you "Feel-good-about-yourself," you can take the next step: making a list of the ways you usually satisfy this need for approval, which most likely is through performing your Ego- References.

Then you find out what your Hidden Agenda is for each one of these Ego-References. This will give you insight into what your ultimate Hidden Goal actually is, and you may discover that this goal no longer serves you. This can become your moment of truth in which you will be ready to let go of what used to be your Hidden Goal in favor of a purpose of your own choosing.

5. *What is a good way to started with questioning your motives?*
You can start by asking yourself the well-known question: WHY do I do what I do?

In other words: Monitor what motivates you during the course of your day, and recognize how these motivations are influencing your present reality.

Then reflect on the following question: Where does the urge to comply with all those rules and to live up to all those conditions come from?

Are these rules and conditions really based on your own insights? If you come to the conclusion that this is not the case, decide to "reprogram" your subconscious mind.

You do this by rethinking all these inherited criteria and opinions, but this time by thinking with your own mind and letting your own heart speak. Let your voice and the expression of your emotion break through! And, above all, be honest with yourself.

Unit 7

1. *What does it mean to be Enmeshed with your parent?*
When you are in an Enmeshment situation, you haven't been able to detach yourself from your parent. You could say that the umbilical cord wasn't cut successfully. This emotional intertwinement can be so strong that you may even depend on that moment of getting your parent's (or other caregiver's) approval to experience feeling alive.

So, it's not surprising that, on a daily basis, you're doing your very best to put that smile on your caregiver's face and get that approval.

Enmeshment happens if you haven't been given the building blocks to develop a Healthy SoS, but instead, have been forced to develop strategies to get approval, which replaces true acknowledgement of you as your own person.

All these individual strategies become a part of what the SoS Method calls your Early Childhood Survival Strategy, which in its totality is aimed at gaining that approval. The approval makes you "Feel-good-about-self." And this state of "Feeling-good-about-self" functions as a substitute for your Sense of Self.

Later, this entire structure becomes the blueprint for how you function as a person. It then is stored in your subconscious mind where it becomes your autopilot. It'll make you select people and situations that allow you to mimic and act out this initial blueprint.

2. Give a few practical examples of how Enmeshment with a parent can show up in a child or adult.

In an Enmeshment situation, you have internalized your parent's preferences and criteria and you have a need to identify yourself with them because that makes you feel safe. So you have a tendency to copy them in specific ways, for example, by eating specific foods your parent loves, or by buying specific gadgets or little trinkets for yourself that your parent might appreciate.

Note that it has never occurred to you to develop your own tastes and preferences, so you tend to do things your parent likes, even when choosing a career or a partner.

By doing so, you're creating a virtual experience of making your parent "Feel-good" and with that you're providing yourself with that much-needed sense of safety.

Again, you have never asked yourself what you really like or want. Unfortunately, you aren't aware of this unhealthy situation because it has always been that way. So, you think that this is how it is supposed to be.

3. What is the root cause of Enmeshment?

Let's look at this problem from the child's perspective. Later, you might want to try seeing this from the parental angle so you can deepen your understanding of both sides of this type of relationship.

The main cause of Enmeshment is based on the fact that your parent is unable to step outside of his or her own world and is mainly focused on him or herself during your childhood. That means that your parent is unable to really "see" you as your own person.

It may very well be that your parent is in need of securing their own "Feel-good-about-self" state. This forces them to control and manipulate you in order to ensure you won't hinder their process.

This is a setting where there is no room for a true relationship with mutual understanding and respect. What you are being taught is to focus on getting approval, instead of on building your own Sense of your Self.

So, you never grow your own "mental spine"; instead, you use your talents to establish what you have to do and how you have to be in order to get approval.

4. How does the internalization of a parental voice take place?

The Internalized Parental Voice (IPV) emerges all by itself, through the repeated verbal and nonverbal messages you, as a child, receive from your parents. In your childish, emotional world, these messages turn into indisputable truths about who you are.

Imagine, for example, that your mother always criticized you, saying things like: "Oh please! You're always ill; there's always something wrong with you; you are a pain in the neck!" Later in life, this so called "truth" may instantly come to mind when you are confronted with—or even just remember—your mother's facial expression that was connected with this kind of reproach.

The IPV is related to the Sense of Self term *Mirroring*.

5. *How does an Internalized Parental Voice typically manifest?*

Your IPV is expressed by you copying your parent's opinions, tastes, and preferences, and by using their values to judge yourself (and others!). It can also show up as a physical symptom, caused by the fear of what might happen if you were to counteract the conditions for getting your parent's approval or were unable to live up to them (for Fear of Annihilation).

Some physical symptoms include extreme tension in neck and shoulders, back pain, headaches, migraines, maybe tinnitus, and certain forms of sleeplessness, which can all be indications of the presence of an Internalized Parental Voice within you.

Unit 8

1. *Specify the terms that relate to becoming dependent on a Substitute SoS for your Self-experience.*

The concepts related to becoming dependent on a Substitute SoS are firstly, the distorted parental Mirror, which gives you, as a child, the message that you are not the way you 'ought to' be. This forces you to turn your attention toward finding out how you should be instead. From then on, you are so thoroughly engaged in these efforts that you miss out on developing a sense of your own Self. This situation leads to a Lack of Sense of Self.

Going hand in hand with the distorted mirror is the growing Fear of Annihilation, which leads to a permanent need for approval as a substitute for the acknowledgement you didn't receive. This is because getting that approval gives you, as a child, the feeling that at least for this moment you are allowed to be.

This need for approval then develops into an Early Childhood Survival Strategy, which leads to a compulsive cycle of executing

Ego References with their Hidden Agendas, so the Hidden Goal that serves as a SSoS can be reached.

2. *In what way is Annihilation related to death?*

The term Annihilation has nothing to do with death but is used in the Sense of Self Method to express the terror of: experiencing yourself as being alive, but not being noticed by others; of having the feeling that, although you are present as a body, your essence has no influence on your surroundings; the experience of living like a ghost because you feel neither seen nor heard.

3. Why does the Fear of Annihilation play such a sabotaging role in whatever you are doing?

The Fear of Annihilation is responsible for a great deal of stress in your life. Why? Because it makes you dependent on a Substitute SoS. The fear of not being able to gain that Substitute SoS adds undue pressure to the tasks you are performing, because rather than doing things for their own sake (Direct Motivation), they function as Vehicles to reach your Hidden Goal.

And although this procedure reduces or eliminates the Fear of Annihilation, you risk failing to get a good quality result in WHAT you are doing, because you are not totally focused on the content of your action or activity.

4. Describe the relationship between (the Fear of) Annihilation and the Hidden Goal.

The more you feel rejected by your parents, the stronger your experience of Annihilation and the more urgent the need to reach your Hidden Goal, because it works as your Substitute SoS, which eliminates the Fear of Annihilation.

When, as a child, you don't feel "seen" by your parent, you already feel non-existence. This feeling carries over into adulthood, and if you don't reach your Hidden Goal it can lead to an intense Fear of Annihilation, which can manifest itself as a deep depression.

5. True or false: Once you experience the Substitute Sense of Self you are fine!

False! A Substitute SoS is a deficient placeholder for your true Self- Experience. It fills in the emptiness where your Sense of Self should be. It may give you an artificial backbone from which you can base decisions, but these are not really your own authentic choices. A Substitute SoS makes you completely dependent on and at the mercy of others. Therefore, the dependency on a Substitute SoS is a condition that has to be undone as soon as possible. You do this by restoring your own Sense of Self, which results in shifting from Indirect Motivation to Direct Motivation, and replacing your Hidden Goal by a healthy life's purpose of your own.

Unit 9

1. Where does the Distorted Mirror fit in the Substitute Sense of Self– Oriented System?

The Distorted Mirror leads to the Lack of Sense of Self, and the resulting dependency on a Substitute Sense of Self leads to the development of a Substitute SoS–Oriented System.

This takes place as you grow up, when your parent/caregiver mirrors back to you an image of you based of his or her own parental needs ("You are not the way I want you to be") and not based on your needs as a child. It occurs when you, as a child, are not seen and treated as your own independent little human being. You then become dependent on parental approval, which you try to gain by fitting into the Distorted Mirror.

An army.
Through the years, this strategy turns into a habit, and even into an addiction, which is stored in every cell of your body.

Visualize the Substitute SoS–Oriented System as an army. The different aspects that make up the totality of who you are—as you have become under the influence of your compulsive need for approval—are like individual soldiers, and each one is aiming at the same target: gaining a Substitute SoS.

Once you've been conditioned to be dependent on that Substitute SoS, this army occupies your being on all levels—body, mind, and emotions—and is mobilized each time an opportunity to gain a Fgas state appears.

2. *What are some parts of a Substitute Sense of Self–Oriented System?*

Your list may include: Self-blame, inauthenticity, Annihilation, the Fear of Annihilation, Early Childhood Survival Strategies with the accompanying Ego-References, Hidden Agendas, Hidden Goal, Vehicles, Internalized Parental Voice, and "Feel-good-about-self" State. Various behavioral or emotional aspects like anger, rage, depression, compulsion, high stress, anxiety, self-sabotage, erratic behavior, fear of your own behavior, fear of your own emotions, fear of other people's behaviors and emotions, fear of failure, and fear of not being able to function. Anything else that causes and/or results in a Lack of Sense of Self.

3. *In the Sense of Self Method, what is a person's most important motivation for realizing a Substitute Sense of Self–Oriented Goal (Hidden Goal)?*

Initially your motivation to realize this goal is inspired by your natural need to feel acknowledged as your own person and see your existence confirmed by those who raised you. If this doesn't occur, your most important motivation will be to gain their approval instead.

This approval is needed if you end up with a Lack of a Sense of Self. Without that approval, you feel Annihilated. This approval produces a "Feel-good-about-self" state that acts as a Substitute Sense of Self.

Acknowledgments

Questioning the role your caregivers have played in your life is uncomfortable for many people. Moreover, even though I had a hard time persuading my friends to read my manuscript and listen to my theory, those who ended up being touched by its content have been tremendously dedicated and helpful in producing this book. They are the ones who have taken care of the ten to twelve rounds of edits the material needed in order to be presented in a way that is coordinated enough to be understandable. Therefore, I can hardly say I wrote this book by myself.

Since 2008, numerous dedicated people have been involved, and I would like to thank them from the depths of my heart. Without you, this book would have stayed in Pandora's Box. Its content would have remained interesting to me but inaccessible to others, and very few people would have been able to make sense of it. Maybe no one would have wanted to open the box in the first place because the benefits would not have been clear and the content would have looked too scary. But thanks to all of your insights, effort, and time, we have here the verbalization of a solution to so many problems that now lies in the hands of the person suffering from them. Thank you all tremendously for seeing the big picture with me and spending your time and energy on getting my story and theory into shape so that others can benefit from it.

Let me begin with profusely thanking Alia Aurami, who was among the first to listen to what I had to say and verify the validity of it. Alia was also instrumental in writing up the first version of the Sense of Self Theory, which is still available at www.holispsych.com. Many people still find this first writing very useful and enlightening.

My heartfelt thanks go to Deborah Drake and Nora Smith, who have been consistently on my side as language sources and transformers of the conclusions I drew from my own challenges, making them more publically accessible. Thank you for never being bored or annoyed with the content, and thank you for your gracious patience to arrive at the point where we are now. In the early stages of Healthy Sense of Self, we did not work remotely. We worked together more often, and I happily recall the memorable circles of discussion about the jargon, about how to best choose the words, how to best describe them, and how to craft the best definitions. The nature of our jargon is a funny one as it turned out to be a subject with a life of its own. It never seemed to be finished, but in written text, you have to settle on something. So, thank you all for your valuable insights and also for staying true to your own opinions when we had to debate, at great length, until an agreement was found.

I thank my daughter Laura for her dedication and patience to producing the prototypes of what has become our brand, character, and illustration style. I am thankful to Marco Scozzi, who has picked up her style, trying to stay close while giving his own take on the artwork.

There were people who came and went over the last seven years whom I would also like to mention and thank: Lily Burns, Michael Maine, and Bookmasters.

Thanks also to Jolene Spath, Leighah Beadle-Darcy, Werner Vogels, and Kim Vogels. I want to specifically express my gratitude for the work done by my longtime friend Gianluigi Ottobrini in Novara, Italy. Thank you for translating the book into Italian; know that from our discussions, I learned so much, and it has greatly contributed to enhancing this book.

Thank you to Marielle Higler and Ilse Wortelboer for taking the material and translating it into Dutch, and discussing the issues that came up. See our Dutch website gezondzelfgevoel.nl.

Thank you to all the people behind those who helped me: their families, their friends, and their connections.

Special thanks to our beta readers. Your courage to be critical and honest about the material has made a noticeable difference.

Thank you.

Short overview of the Sense of Self Method

A Healthy Sense of Self is the felt sense of being your own person, separate from others. With a Healthy Sense of Self, you are free to be the unique human being you were born to be. It allows you to effectively become increasingly more independent through each stage of development. A Sense of Self (SoS) is cultivated from birth, but only when your primary caregivers truly see and acknowledge you as an autonomous being, as opposed to (unknowingly) considering you to be an extension of themselves or considering you to be a burden. A Healthy Sense of Self is profoundly significant because it is the foundation for living an authentic life, a life without shame, regret, or anxiety, as opposed to a lifetime of addiction to approval.

The Sense of Self Method is a self-help program that allows you to determine if you have a Healthy Sense of Self and, if one is lacking, helps you to build a Restored Sense of Self. Restoring your Sense of Self ultimately leads to living and functioning as if you had a Natural Healthy Sense of Self. Chances are that, just like a person with a Healthy Sense of Self, you too will develop more inner peace and vitality, your relationship skills will improve, and your overall quality of life will greatly increase.

Abstract of the Sense of Self Method

INTRODUCTION

Insomnia and many other mental, emotional, and physical imbalances are part of a wide array of human suffering that share one root cause: a Lack of Sense of Self. Restoring one's Sense of Self dismantles many, if not all resulting aspects of ill health and lack of well-being.

The purpose of my studies was to discover the underlying cause of the sudden onset of insomnia that commenced after the birth of my first daughter (1985), as I resumed work as a bassoonist in the Amsterdam Philharmonic Orchestra.

My studies have resulted in multiple books and an online course about the Sense of Self Method. I developed this method to help people restore their Sense of Self and recognize that their motivation for doing or avoiding things often has nothing to do with who they really are and what they would want for themselves. Posing the question, "WHY do you do/want/avoid WHAT you do/want/avoid?" inspires people to look behind the scenes of their motivation. Then they start to see what drives them and envision the conclusion that being so estranged from their real self may have led to the symptoms of disease they are experiencing.

The intention of this abstract is to invite academically trained professionals, especially psychologists, to investigate the validity of my approach and, if deemed relevant, take steps to test my conclusions by conducting studies on a larger scale.

THE PROBLEM

At the time (1985) I sought treatment no relevant cure for insomnia was available in the medical field. I had to take matters into my own hands. My goal was to end my insomnia, restore my well-being, and get my life back on track.

In the process I noticed within myself an array of other issues, including but not limited to rage, fear of my own emotions, the need to manipulate other people and control circumstances, the lack of any spontaneous moments of happiness, as well as a workaholic behavior.

Through deep exploration into the subconsciously motivated mental and emotional reactions I displayed to daily challenges, I concluded these were all driven by a single factor: the urgent need to compensate for the absence of a Healthy Sense of Self.

This discovery led to my understanding that a myriad of other issues could be connected to that same root cause: difficulties in childrearing, relationship issues, insomnia, anxiety and depression, anger management issues, weight problems and eating DO, addictive behaviors, domestic violence, fear of failure, performance anxiety, loneliness, lack of empathy and compassion, the inability to work within or contribute to groups on the job or in the world at large.

And possibly: Alzheimer's disease and other forms of dementia, fibromyalgia, labelled disorders such as bipolar DO, ADHD, and many more.

THE METHOD

I am not academically trained as a psychologist, but I consider myself a (self-made) motivation expert.

My method of collecting data and drawing conclusions has been performing ongoingly introspection, recording, and reviewing of my thoughts, feelings, and findings for over 30 years (1995 – 2015). Labelling my thoughts and feelings provided me with the tools to map out my inner processes and draw consistent conclusions. Asking the question, *"Why* do/did I do *what* I do/did?" and being brutally honest with myself has been instrumental in this approach.

Observing others to discover which essential piece of the puzzle they possessed that I was missing, helped me come to my conclusions about the overarching effects on behavior of a Sense of Self or the lack thereof.

THE RESULTS

I discovered that the various disrupting symptoms I experienced had one cause in common: a Lack of Sense of Self (LoSoS). A LoSoS is caused by inadequate Mirroring of the child by her caregivers. When a person is prevented from developing a Healthy Sense of Self in childhood, she becomes dependent on approval. Earning that parental smile makes her "Feel-good-about-herself". It gives her a fleeting moment of feeling worthy, which then is mistaken for a Sense of Self. This cycle of dependency on approval for self-validation functions as a substitute for the missing connection to the Real self (Substitute Sense of Self (SSoS)).

Because of the life-and-death urgency to fill the void in the self-experience, a need develops to perform perfectly. This is particularly relevant for the self-imposed conditions a person with a LoSoS tends to use (and persists in using) to convince her caregiver that she is worthy of his or her attention. These conditions vary individually as they are founded on what one learns in childhood regarding the successes and failures in earning approval.

The dependency on approval, if not addressed, is carried over into adulthood and leads to an overwhelming amount of stress that can result in a great variety of mental, emotional, and physical symptoms.

Through guided introspection, the Sense of Self Method offers insight into the devastating consequences of motivations that are geared towards gaining a Substitute Sense of Self. It provides exercises in body awareness, visualizations, and self-affirmations as a path to a Restored Sense of Self.

CONCLUSION

What are the implications of this finding? Restoring one's Sense of Self is the answer to the seemingly unrelated array of problems and issues caused by a LoSoS. The moment one's focus shifts from the need to gain approval to experiencing unconditional self-acceptance, many of the symptoms disappear naturally.

Numerous benefits come with this approach because it enables people, to a large extent, to work things out for themselves. This results in fewer office visits, and, consequently, lower healthcare costs. Symptomatic treatment of ailments that result from a LoSoS seem to be a waste of time, money, and effort.

The immediate result of a Restored Sense of Self is less stress, better health and well-being, improved quality of life, and a higher degree of self-actualization. It also leads to more responsible and adequate child rearing for parents of young children. These positive changes are also reflected in fewer absences from work or school, and a greater sense of personal satisfaction.

If mine is a relevant finding, I would hope that more official, scientifically based conclusions will enable implementation of the Sense of Self Principle in the various modalities of healing. It is my dream to make Sense of Self counselors available in educational settings from elementary schools to universities and other institutes of professional education.

As a potential limitation I envision that my approach might, at best, be considered an extensive case study. However, it is not up to me to draw conclusions as I consider it immoral to withhold from the appropriate sources any information that might have the potential of being beneficial to the greater good.

About the Author

Antoinetta Vogels was born in 1946 in the Netherlands at the end of World War II. She vividly recalls listening to her father's stories about the horrors of the war, while walking with him through the ruins of his native city, Groningen. She made the firm decision, even as a young girl, that she herself had to do something *to make wars stop*!

Little did Antoinetta know that life would offer her an opportunity to contribute to the understanding of human behavior by having her grow up with a "Lack of Sense of Self," and therefore providing her with the task of figuring out what was "missing" in her life.

As an accomplished bassoonist in several professional classical orchestras in the Netherlands, Antoinetta was a disciplined performer who enjoyed the creativity and expression of her work.

Motherhood resulted in two lovely daughters and the sudden onset of severe insomnia, which forced her into early retirement from her musical career early. This is where Antoinetta's inner journey began in determining the underlying cause of the predicament that continued plaguing her for over twenty-five years: insomnia.

Antoinetta started out with continuous introspection. Next she began recording her thoughts and feelings, a process that enabled her to identify patterns of behavior, and ultimately led to her Sense of Self Theory.

Antoinetta's mission is to share how a Healthy Sense of Self is a crucial asset for each individual and for the world at large (Peace)!

Antoinetta lived in her homeland until 1995, when she moved with her family to Ithaca, NY. She later moved to Seattle, where she has been writing and speaking for almost a decade now.

Through her company, Healthy Sense of Self®, Antoinetta offers education and techniques that restore one's Sense of Self.

"A Healthy Sense of Self
is the backbone of the human psyche.
Without it a person skips his/her own life altogether."

Vision and Mission Statement of Healthy Sense Of Self®

VISION

Our Company strives to provide insight and deliver strategies that contribute to increase significantly the overall quality of life of the individual and ultimately of the world at large. HySoS helps in increasing or restoring a Healthy Sense of Self in the individual which immediately leads to improving health, productivity, success, well-being and peace. Healthy SenseOfSelf ® strives to expand this message in ever-increasingly diverse, effective, and well-utilized ways for ever-increasing numbers of individuals and groups so that this effect spreads outward in ripples, developing a momentum and life of its own.

MISSION STATEMENT

We believe that the world can be a better place and HySoS contributes to our envisioned world by developing and delivering both education and activities for making our Sense of Self healthier. Our specific ways of educating and providing activities for that purpose include, but are not limited to: offering information to individuals and to groups in the form of conferences, teleconferences, seminars and teleseminars, webinars online and/or real life –courses with potentially a Train-the-Trainers Program, educational speeches and presentations, podcasts, video's, radio and-TV appearances, articles in Journals, Newspapers and Magazines, a Newsletters, potentially our own Ezine. Our ultimate dream is: a HySoS –Foundation comprising of treatment and educational facilities, with national as well as international franchises.

HySoS strives to help people (re-)align with who they really are by strengthening or Restoring their Sense of Self ®. Thus, we work specifically with parents, teachers, teacher-trainers, clergy, speakers, and others who influence many people, so we educate the educators for maximum scope of impact on the world. We also provide opportunities for both our employees and those we reach in other ways to gain full understanding and full benefits from this integrated non-medical method. We strive to be business as well as family, thus providing what's missing in many people's lives: a sense of purpose and home.

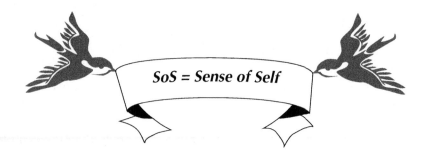

SoS = Sense of Self

Overview HySoS Resources

WEBSITES AND BLOGS:

https://www.healthysenseofself.com/

WEBSITE NETHERLANDS:

https://www.gezondzelfgevoel.nl

WEBSITE ITALY:

https://www.sanosensodise.it

FACEBOOK:

https://www.facebook.com/Healthysenseofself

FACEBOOK NETHERLANDS:

https://www.facebook.com/GezondZelfGevoel

FACEBOOK ITALY:

https://www.facebook.com/SanoSensodiSe

INSTAGRAM UNITED STATES:

https://instagram.com/healthysenseofself

INSTAGRAM NETHERLANDS:

https://instagram.com/gezondzelfgevoel_nl

TWITTER:

https://twitter.com/healthysos

LINKEDIN USA:

https://www.linkedin.com/in/annetvogels

AUTHOR'S AMAZON.COM:

https://amazon.com/Antoinetta-Vogels/e/B00JBFU1SG

AUTHOR OF:

- *Healthy Sense of Self - How to be true
to your Self and make your world a better place*

- *Online Course: Introducing
the Sense of Self Method*

- *The Sense of Self Help! Workbook*

- *The Motivation Cure -
The secret to being your best Self*

- *A Guided Journal to a Healthy Sense of Self:
Thoughts to Inspire Peace Within and Around
the World*

- *How to overcome insomnia all by yourself*

NETHERLANDS:

- *Gezond Zelf-Gevoel: Dé Methode om het
beste uit Jezelf te halen*

- *Online Cursus: de Zelf-Gevoel Methode*

- *Werkboek voor de Zelf-Gevoel Methode (gebaseerd op de onlinecursus maar ook onafhankelijk te gebruiken)*

- *Het Gezond Zelf-Gevoel Dagboekje - Een inspiratiebron voor persoonlijke en wereldvrede*

- *Slapeloosheid - Hoe kom je er vanaf?*

ITALY:

- *Diario Guidato a un Sano Senso di Sé: 120 pratici suggerimenti per riconquistare la propria vita*

CONTACTS:

- Email: contact@healthysenseofself.com

NETHERLANDS:

- Email: info@gezondzelfgevoel.nl

ITALY:

- Email: info@sanosensodise.it

Printed in Great Britain
by Amazon

14913789R00149